The *Old Devon* FARMHOUSE

AN ILLUSTRATED STUDY AND CATALOGUE OF
THE DEVON FARMHOUSE COLLECTION

Peter Brears

DEVON BOOKS

First published in Great Britain by Devon Books 1998

ISBN 1 85522 626 X

Cataloguing in Publication Data

CIP record for this title is available from the British Library

DEVON BOOKS

OFFICIAL PUBLISHER TO DEVON COUNTY COUNCIL

Halsgrove House
Lower Moor Way
Tiverton, Devon, UK
EX16 6SS

Tel: 01884 243242
Fax: 01884 243325
http://www.halsgrove.com

Printed in Great Britain by Bookcraft Ltd, Midsomer Norton.

Contents

Charles Hey Laycock (1879-1944) the great collector and writer on Devon farmhouse life, sitting at the fireside of the traditional kitchen he set up in his Moretonhampstead home.

Acknowledgements

The publication of this catalogue has been greatly assisted through the sponsorship of Miss Christine Legge, Honorary Secretary of the Torquay Natural History Society. I am also most grateful to Dr Michael Bishop, Curator of the Torquay Museum, Mr Barry Chandler, Assistant Curator, and all their staff for their considerable assistance, good company and tea while working on the collections, and to Mr Ronald Casey, Honorary Librarian of the Torquay Natural History Society, for access to its fine library. Mr Len Harvey of Heavitree and Mrs Edna White of St Marychurch both provided very useful memories of the late Mr C.H.Laycock, Mrs M. Tibbott, Mr J.Malden and Mr M. Watts provided further useful information, and Ms Elizabeth Prince of Mearsdon Manor gave me ready access to his former home. I would also like to thank Mr Terry and Mrs Sandra Stephens of the Shirley Hotel for making my visits to Torquay over the past two years such an enjoyable experience.

Introduction

Any visitor to Devon is immediately struck by the strong regional character of its countryside, whether on the high tors and wild open spaces of Dartmoor, or in the rich farming country, with its rolling hills, high hedges and narrow lanes. Virtually none of this is as nature intended, for over the course of thousands of years various peoples have modified it to meet their particular needs. As in all parts of Europe, it has been occupied by incoming prehistoric groups, followed by the Romans and a series of continental invaders, terminating with the Normans. They each contributed something to the distinctive Devonian blend of land-use, buildings, artefacts, language, customs and beliefs which gradually developed over the following millennia. The best place to observe this characteristic life-style was the old Devon farm. Many of its individual features and practices could be found throughout Europe and other parts of the world, but here in Devon they had been evolved and adapted to make the best possible use of the local environment. Nowhere else could anyone find the rich combination of cob walls, reed thatch, fine cooperage, cloam ovens, wheel bellows, Dartmoor kettles, clotted cream, handmade butter, white ale, distinctive regional patterns of furniture and dialect words etc. once in everyday use on the Devon farm.

Today, in a world dominated by rapid communications, mass production, and a prodigal consumer society, it can be difficult to imagine the English rural scene up to the 1870s when news, goods and people could never travel faster than a horse. Trains, barges and coastal shipping did provide good services between the major towns and ports, but still bypassed vast areas of this country. As a result, the rural communities remained both static and largely self-sufficient in those basic foods and services required for everyday life. Over the next half century, however, the picture altered completely. Radio, motorised transport, increasing factory production, and conscription during the war of 1914-18 were among a whole mass of developments which transformed every aspect of our traditional lifestyles.

In Devon, a number of highly observant and committed individuals realised that they were living through a period of unprecedented change. They saw fine old buildings, furniture, domestic and farming equipment, dialect, song and dance, all representing important aspects of their rich regional culture, being discarded in favour of standardised versions imported from distant cosmopolitan urban centres. Since no one else appeared to care about this, they decided that they would use their own resources of time, energy and considerable capital to record and collect as much as possible about traditional Devon life, especially that lived in the farmhouses of Dartmoor and the South Hams.

Although they took great pleasure in this work, it was not an entirely selfish activity, for their aim was to provide a permanent body of information and artefacts for the enjoyment and education of present and future generations. For these reasons, they published as much of their information as they could, gave their collections to the Torquay Natural History Society, and provided funds worth hundreds of thousands of pounds in today's values, to create galleries, cases and conservation budgets so that their collections could be fully displayed and preserved at the Torquay Museum. Their Devon Farmhouse Collection has now been there for over half a century, its importance being ever more appreciated as the years progress.

One of the great problems with any museum collection is its accessibility and interpretation. Most museums conceal the bulk of their collections and related information from the public, largely due to a lack of resources, and it can be virtually impossible for individuals to discover just what is lurking in their stores and records. Academics, students, collectors, curators, teachers, film set designers, television researchers, craftworkers, re-enactors, local historians, and any interested members of the public should have the same ready access to resources in museums as they already enjoy to those in public libraries and record offices. The real practical difficulty in achieving this is often due to the very nature of the specimens. Bulky, fragile and perhaps unique, they are always at risk when being moved or handled. The traditional solution to these problems, for some three hundred years, has been to publish the collection in the form of a printed catalogue. This is a time-consuming and costly business, but its benefits are considerable. It makes it possible for anyone, in this country or elsewhere, to discover what the museum contains, and all the relevant known information, by simply lifting down a book, and browsing through its pages.

Drawings are usually better than photographs in clearly showing the appearance and construction of each specimen, enabling a considerable amount of information to become readily available without the trouble and expence of travelling long distances, and without risk of physically damaging the original specimens. A catalogue also gives a degree of security to the specimens, ensuring that their appearance and information will always be available, even if, through accident or design, the original material is ever lost or destroyed. For these reasons, it was decided that the present catalogue of the Devon Farmhouse Collection should be published, in preparation for its re-display at the Torquay Museum.

Here the story of the collectors and the collection is first presented, this being followed by a tour of a Devon farmhouse as it was before the 1860s, explaining where and how each artefact was used. Finally, there comes the catalogue itself, which describes each item in turn, arranged according to the Social History and Industrial Classification.

It is, in many ways, a pioneering work, nothing on this scale having been published before in England, but hopefully it will prove worthy of the collections in advancing the interest, enjoyment and appreciation of traditional Devon farmhouse life, and the wealth of artefacts associated with it.

Peter Brears
Leeds, 1997

Collectors and Collecting

When studying the traditional material culture of these islands in general, and the Devon Farmhouse Collection in particular, it soon becomes obvious that this subject was at its most popular in the 1890–1930 period. It was at this time that most of the really significant collections were formed, and the bulk of the current body of primary publications made its appearance. The reasons for this surge of interest may be largely attributed to two major factors. The first of these was a direct reaction to the unparalleled explosion of urbanisation and industrialisation during the late nineteenth century, and its disruption of the centuries-old highly regional and occupational patterns of living. The second, meanwhile, was the existence of a leisured class with incomes derived from the land, the church, the Empire, or the assets accumulated from Britain's phenomenal industrial growth, which provided them with the resources to develop their personal research interests and to collect as a fashionable hobby.

Even in the eighteenth century, the gentry and the clergy had begun to collect and study both artefacts and 'popular antiquities', as folk song, calendar customs and various other traditions were then known, this being continued into the nineteenth century, as shown by publications such as William Hone's *Every-Day Book* of 1826, or William Howitt's *Rural Life of England* of 1838, and the journals of numerous county archaeological societies. From the later nineteenth century this movement, strongly influenced by the writings of William Morris (1834-1896) and his followers, took on a much more aesthetic and material-oriented approach. This valued for their own sake the beauty, sympathetic construction and refined fitness of purpose inherent in the bulk of artefacts made and used in traditional households and occupations. Architects such as Philip Webb (1831-1915) and Norman Shaw (1831-1912) began to adopt vernacular features into their buildings, while designer/craftworker/writers such as Gertrude Jekyll (1843-1932) introduced the public to the importance of collecting 'common things of everyday use, articles of furniture and ordinary household gear that I remember in every cottage and farmhouse' as described in her highly influential *Old West Surrey* of 1904. Other classic books of this period include Richard Heath's *The English Peasant* of 1893, Hastings Neville's *A Corner in the North* of 1909, Adelaide Gosset's *Shepherds of Britain* of 1911, Sidney Jones' *The Village Homes of England* of 1912, and the *Chats on...* series, including Fred Burgess' *Chats on Household Curios* of 1912.

Further evidence of popular awareness of the need to preserve elements of the past about this time is provided by the founding of the Society for the Preservation of Ancient Buildings in 1877, followed by the National Trust in 1895.[1]

In many ways, the rural cottage and farmhouse provided ideal subjects for study and collecting. Their garden features, vernacular architecture, craftsman-made furniture, fittings and equipment were still extant in substantial quantities, even though major changes were taking place. As Gertrude Jekyll had stated, such items were now being sold as curiosities and antiquities. Cottages, whose furniture and equipment had passed through several generations, were being re-equipped with cheap pretentious articles, got up with veneer and varnish, and other shoddy material. Their floors were being covered with oil-cloth, their walls with paper of shocking design, and hung with cheap oleographs and

tradesmen's illustrated almanacs. This was the modern exchange for the solid furniture of pure material and excellent design, all the best possible for their varied purposes, which had evolved throughout the centuries.[2] The discovery and collection of such material was not seen as an end in itself, but as part of a comprehensive survey which recorded its use, its dialect names, and any associated customs and beliefs which, along with rites of passage, calendar customs, folk song, etc., made up the entirety of the fast-disappearing lifestyle of the countryside.[3] In Devon, the outstanding collector and recorder of such material was Charles H. Laycock (1879-1943), as may be seen in his collections in the Torquay Museum.

Founded in 1844, the Torquay Natural History Society is one of the oldest private organisations of its kind which still operates an excellent museum for the public, and a fine library and lecture series for its members. As early as 1847, it had already decided 'to confine the Museum objects to Devonian specimens, believing that a complete local Museum would be more interesting to members and to prove more attractive to scientific strangers than an imperfect general collection would be'.[4] This sound policy, now continued for 150 years, has stood the test of time, and enabled the museum to build up an exceptionally fine regional collection covering all aspects of geology and other natural sciences, archaeology, the decorative arts and social history.

Its first major excursion into collecting local folk-life or social history artefacts took place in the 1890s, under the influencial presidency of Dr Paul Quick Karkeek, who held this office from 1893 to 1896.[5] Born in Truro in September 1843, he had been educated at Probus School and St Bartholomew's Hospital London, where he qualified as a surgeon. After working as a house surgeon at Chester Infirmary and the Seaman's Hospital, Greenwich, and finally completing his training in France and Germany, he purchased his practice and moved to Torquay around 1874. Here he was appointed Medical Officer of Health in 1878, but these professional duties did not distract him from his passionate interest in local history.[6] His special interest was Devon in the Civil War period, and during the last quarter of the century he gave frequent lectures and published a score of papers on this and related subjects.[7] His lively and interesting style can still be appreciated in his 'Notes made during a visit to Exmoor and Neighbourhood' which he read to the Torquay Natural History Society on 29 October 1879. Here, for example, we learn that his dinner at the Luttrell Arms, Dunster, was of 'Hashed venison and whortle-berry tart - very good'! It was probably on such journeys that he discovered the exceptionally rare group of pack-horse equipment which he presented to the museum. The 1908 museum guide notes that 'Round the walls of the Museum, above the wall-cases are arranged a few objects of local antiquarian interest, chiefly collected by the late Dr Karkeek. These include some old pack saddles, reversible plough, man-trap, ox-yoke, and stocks, cheese presses, spinning wheels and wool-carding machines'.[8] Unfortunately Dr Karkeek had died following a stroke when preparing a lecture in December 1902, but in his will he left his choice library of 2067 volumes to the Society, together with £50 for additional purchases.[9]

Further major donations began to be received in 1918-1919, when Mr R.P. Chope gave 'eight specimens of obsolete agricultural implements, [with] an illustrated paper describing them'.[10] Mr Chope was born at Hartland, North Devon, and grew up there on the farm occupied by his family since 1721. After graduating from Trinity College, Cambridge, he entered the Patent Office in 1884, where he continued to work for the next 38 years. Although he lived in north London throughout this period, he continued an incredibly productive life-long interest in Devon and its history, as may be seen in his extensive bibliography published posthumously in his *Book of Hartland* of 1940. As sometime editor

of the *London Devonian Yearbook, Devon and Cornwall Notes and Queries, The Transactions of the Devonshire Association*, and a contributor to Joseph Wright's *English Dialect Dictionary* he was in regular correspondence with virtually everyone active in this field. His various papers on church ales, cottage gardens, Crying the Neck, apple tree charms, rural ways, calendar customs, folklore, dialect, and study of St Nectan (see cat.no.2), all illustrate the depth of his knowledge and enthusiasm for every aspect of traditional life in Devon. About the same time two new members joined the society, whose enthusiasm, knowledge and generosity were to greatly enhance the prestige and importance of the museum's collections. The first, Charles H.Laycock of Cross Street, Moretonhampstead, joined in 1917, and the second, Dr and Mrs M.E. Fielden of 2, Rowley Road, St Marychurch, joined in 1920.[11]

In many ways, Charles Laycock provides a classic example of that priviledged generation of Edwardian middle-class collectors who, through the inheritance of accumulated family capital, could afford to devote their entire lives to the furtherance of their personal interests. His ability to build up his collection, house it in complete period settings throughout his lifetime, and then to leave it to Torquay Museum, together with very substantial sums to build the Laycock Gallery, and fund its long-term preservation, was entirely due to the acumen and sagacity of his grandfather, James Campey Laycock.[12]

Born at Appleton near York on 6 May 1796, James Laycock was educated at Tadcaster, before joining Potter's, a firm of Manchester linen bleachers. He soon realised that his vocation lay in other fields, and so began to study the law, first being articled to Mr Russell of York, and then to Messrs Iliffe, Russell and Cardale in London. Admitted as a solicitor in 1819, he moved up to Huddersfield in 1820, establishing his office first in King Street, and later in Lion Arcade, St George's Square. At this time, shortly after the Napoleonic wars, this small Yorkshire textile town stood at the very brink of an amazingly vigorous period of expansion. Vast wealth generated by the introduction of the factory system and steam-powered wool textile machinery, brought in new populations, new transport systems, new housing and public services,and new systems of local government, all of which required the services of a thoroughly competent and efficient young solicitor.

James Laycock realised that the real source of power and influence lay in the administration of the various new organisations, rather than in their formal directorships or presidencies. Within a few years he had become Lieutenant of the Huddersfield Armed Association (1820s), Clerk of the County Magistrates (1823-72), Clerk of the Huddersfield Borough Magistrates (to 1872), promoter and solicitor of the Huddersfield Banking Company (from 1827), honorary secretary to the Huddersfield and Upper Agbrigg Savings Bank, co-secretary of the Huddersfield Dispensary (1821-32) and Infirmary (1832-61), and chairman of the Huddersfield Gas Company. In addition, as a churchwarden, he was largely responsible for the rebuilding of the parish church (1834-6). His educational work included acting as founder of the Collegiate School (1837), the presidency of the Female Educational Institute, secretary and later treasurer of the Day Schools (1841-84), and for over forty years, the teacher and superintendent of the Parish Church Sunday Schools. In contrast, he rather surprisingly acted as secretary to that infamous committee of manufacturers and mill-owners which fought so vociferously against Richard Oastler and his campaign for improving the appalling conditions then being experienced by young factory children.[13]

At the time of his death at the advanced age of 88, in February 1885, he was one of Huddersfield's most respected citizens. His practice had been very successful, but his prosperity had not been diverted into a lavish lifestyle, for he and his family had

continued to live in a modest house at 2, Fitzwilliam Street, close to the town centre.[14] He left three children. One daughter had married the Rev. William Bromley, curate at the parish church, another had married George Dyson, a solicitor who had been taken into partnership before 1863, and a son, William, who had been admitted as a solicitor in 1866, and also taken into the partnership, which practiced as Laycock, Dyson and Laycock.[15]

By 1887 William Laycock had left the old family house and removed to Bryan Lodge, a large house in the fashionable suburb of Edgerton.[16] This would provide a suitably prestigious home for himself, his wife, and his young son Charles Hey Laycock, who had been born on 4 April 1879.[17] In the mid 1890s William finally decided that he had had enough of northern industrial life and, having apparently sold his interest in the family firm to his cousin Thomas James Dyson, he removed to Devon, being recorded in the 1897 directories as William Laycock JP of 'St Michael's', Wolborough Hill, Newton Abbot.

Charles Laycock, now aged 16, attended Newton College for two years, and then went up to Merton Hall, Oxford, where the University Calendar recorded him as a commoner in 1899. Shortly afterwards he returned to his father's house in Newton Abbot, and began to develop his interest in the life and traditions of Devon, joining the Devonshire Association in 1905, and becoming a member of its council in 1909.[18] In many ways this represented a complete rejection of his family's origins and lifestyle. Late Victorian Huddersfield's booming economy, based on woollen mills and their related engineering and chemical industries, produced vast quantities of both 'muck' and 'brass'. It's fine Pennine landscape, with high moors, deep-cut valleys, clear-running streams, and fresh, bracing air, had been hideously blackened by the thousands of coal fires, the mill chimneys, and the mill refuse which poured out ever-increasing volumes of foul pollution each succeeding day. Its social life was equally stifling, as its *nouveau riche* middle-class ladies vied with each other in every aspect of fashionable manners, costume and furnishings. Formal weekly 'At Home' teas, silk dresses, and parlours crammed with every over-designed artefact were *de rigueur* in the prosperous villas of Edgerton.

The move to Wolborough Hill, the wealthy villa community overlooking Newton Abbot, enabled Mr and Mrs Laycock to enjoy the same level of social life in truly idyllic surroundings, but for Charles Laycock there was now a real chance of escape. A few minutes walk from the garden gate of St Michael's the villas stopped, and there, above the medieval parish church, extended the wide prospect of Dartmoor, untamed, unpolluted, and undeveloped, the very antithesis of Victorian Huddersfield. From now on, every aspect of his Yorkshire roots was to be forgotten, as he became a Devon countryman, knowledgeable on every aspect of the county's traditional life, speaking its dialect (when he chose), and singing its songs. He did this with amazing ease, flitting between the respectable, scholarly and essentially affluent world of Charles H. Laycock, gentleman, in Torquay and London, and that of Old Charlie Laycock, singer and old Devon boy, around Dartmoor. Whichever role he adopted, he never appears to have lost the real respect and appreciation of all who had the pleasure and privilege of meeting him.

The easiest way for him to get into Dartmoor (before he bought his motorbike) was to take the South Devon Railway branch from Newton Abbot for twelve miles up to the picturesque town of Moretonhampstead. Here, around 1909, he was able to purchase the block of three traditional buildings at 32 Cross Street, now known as Mearsdon Manor. This was the original manor house, enlarged by the Courtenay's in the early fourteenth century, and still retaining a number of its medieval features. It had fallen on hard times, however, the thatch being over six feet thick due to successive patching, and required

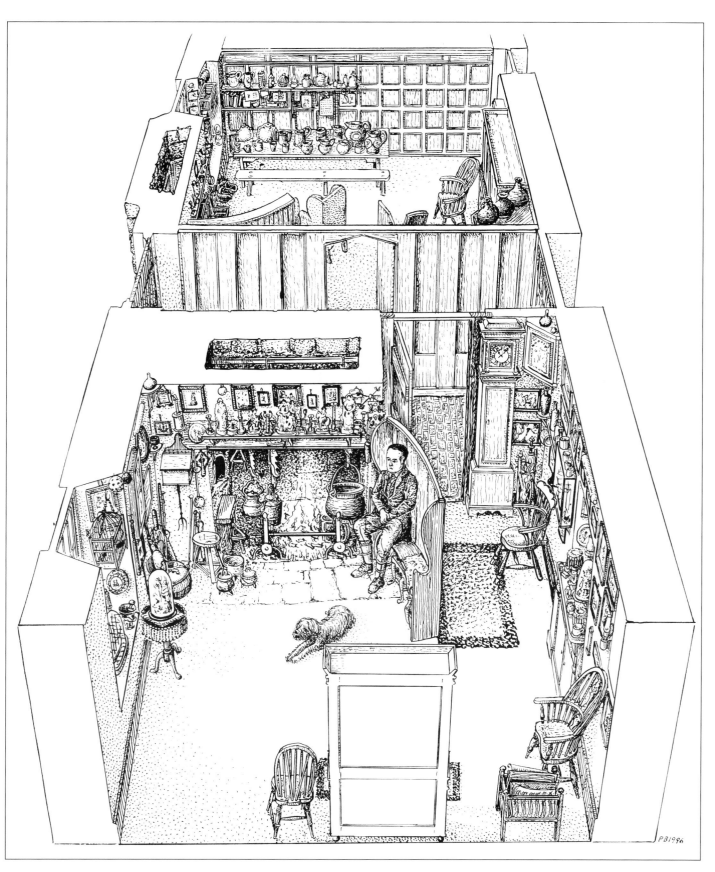

Charles Laycock's front kitchen/parlour (foreground), drang-way or cross-passage (middle) and back kitchen (at top) at Cross Street, Moretonhampstead. Their appearance, around 1910-20, can be meticulously reconstructed from a series of contemporary photographs, the original contents included in the Torquay Museum, and the house itself, which remains virtually unchanged since he lived there.

The Devon farmhouse parlour at Cross Street, Moretonhampstead, showing the witch balls hanging above the window where, according to tradition, they reflected away all evil influences from outside. The truncheon hanging on the wall was a family heirloom, while the American clock is the actual one which hung in the back kitchen of the barton he described.

considerable renovation. To make a comfortable home, the whole of the south front was extended with a new dining room and drawing room, with bedrooms and a balcony above, and the former cottage in the garden transformed into a 'music house' for his growing collection of early keyboard instruments. The original buildings lining Cross Street were altered as little as possible, for here he decided to recreate a Devon farmhouse kitchen, cross-passage and parlour as accurately as possible. Since he considered himself to be 'unfortunately, a good half-century too late to draw my picture entirely from "real life", so to speak, [they apparently presented] a picture of the Devon farmhouse as it was up to the middle of the nineteenth century [rather] than as it is now'.[19] 'For, though much that is old and interesting remains, the interiors of most of the old farm-houses still standing have been to a greater or lesser extent modernised, so as to comply with present-day ideas of comfort and hygene... we may now even find bathrooms served by a modern hot-water system, inside sanitation, and the house may be lit with gas or even electric light. All these "improvements" were quite unknown in our grandfather's days.'

To create his collection, and furnish his period rooms, he acquired 'a good part of the old furniture and utensils [which could] still be found in farm-houses in out-of-the-way country districts, but a large number of things [were] no longer to be met with in their old and once familiar places. With the passing of certain customs and practices from the farmhouse, had gone the implements and utensils intimately connected with those practices. For the... Devon farmer in particular, though strongly conservative, [was] at the same time a practical man, his busy life indeed leaving him but little time to indulge in sentiment... and when once convinced that his old methods were no longer tenable, had no hesitation in making a clean sweep of the old practices and everything connected with them... leaving the old implements and utensils to rot, or selling them for a few shillings to the dealer in scrap-iron, little dreaming that one day many of them would command a fictitious value as objects of antique interest'.

For overall guidance, Charles Laycock referred to Gertrude Jekyll's *Old West Surrey* and to Arthur Hayden's *Chats on Cottage and Farm-house Furniture*, but the great value of his work lay in his own personal research and observation of the fabric, furnishing and use of the Devonshire farm-house or barton.[20] This he published in a major three-part paper entitled 'The Old Devon Farm-house' in the *Transactions of the Devonshire Association*.[21] 'My object in writing this paper', he wrote, 'is to try and place on permanent record a description, with

illustrations as far as possible, of the interior of a typical old Devon farm-house or barton, as it appeared when all its time-honoured articles of furniture, household utensils, and cottage ornaments were still to be found in their accustomed places, in which many of them stood for a couple of centuries or more'. 'Every article has been seen by myself in actual use in one or other of the farmhouses with which I am well acquainted, or else has been accurately described to me by one who has so seen it in use before my time.' In his paper, he conducts the reader on a highly informed and finely observed tour of 'an old Devon barton pulled down some years ago, but drawn according to memories of one he knew well'. It is a masterpiece of folk life or social history writing, virtually unique in its degree of detail and its depth of knowledge, and still well worth reading in its full 113-page entirety.

In addition, it admirably reflects Charles Laycock's passionate desire to preserve the content and entire context of traditional Devon farmhouse interiors as they appeared before their grand fireplaces were blocked up for stoves, their beams masked in matchboard, their lattice windows replaced by sashes, and their handmade furniture superseded by the 'miserable nondescript factory productions of the present day'. The interiors of his house at Moretonhampstead were accurately and authentically furnished to partly fulfill this purpose, as may be seen in the photographs which were taken to illustrate his paper. His ultimate aim was to go much further, however, his views being just as relevant today as when they were penned at the conclusion of his paper in 1924:

> *'I should like to point out the desirability of acquiring and preserving at least one typical example of the old Devon farm-house, with its furniture and utensils intact, before it is too late and they have all been swept away and forgotten. Or, if this could not be conveniently done, the desirability of erecting on some suitable spot... a "life-size" model in lath and plaster, or better still in cob, of a typical old farm-house, complete with its furniture and household utensils, as they appeared up to about fifty years ago.*
>
> *This has been done successfully in Sweden and Denmark, and there seems no reason why it should not be done in this country.*
>
> *With the passing of old farm life, there has been a steadily growing interest taken in old farm-house furniture and utensils in the last twenty years, both by students of native craftsmanship and by lovers of relics of bygone days. And much of this class of furniture has of late years been added to many of our museums.*
>
> *But, if old farm-house furniture is worth preserving at all, due consideration should surely be given as to the best means of exhibiting it. Now there can be no doubt about it how very much more interesting and life-like it appears when exhibited in its natural surroundings within the farm-house, than when displayed in the usual dry-as-dust method of museum arrangement adopted in this country, of rows of chairs and tables, cases of china, etc., without any background. It is like taking a precious jewel out of its setting.*
>
> *Such an undertaking ought not to be impossible... if Devon could lead the way, possibly other counties might be induced to follow suit. So that in time we might have the pleasure of seeing in many of our county towns examples of old farm-houses which might be regarded as typical of certain particular localities, and thus preserve for all time this national heritage bequeathed to us by our forefathers.'*

This was only one way in which Charles Laycock wished to interpret the past for the benefit of the public. He published further papers on aspects of traditional life, and also

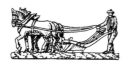

presented lectures on 'Devonshire Speech', 'The Old Devon Farm-house', 'The Wasps of Devonshire' etc.[22] His interest in music was reflected in a fine collection of keyboard stringed instruments at his Moretonhampstead home. Here 'it was a delight to hear him play the harpsichord, spinet and clavichord, and to sing the old tunes he knew so well'.[23] These he demonstrated at public lectures on 'English National and Folk Music, with Folk Songs of Devon', or 'Devonshire Folk Music', both having 'Musical Illustrations'.[24] The Torquay Natural History Society's library has a volume of his manuscript notes of the texts, and usually the melodies, of some of the songs he must have sung on these occasions.[25] They are numbered from 81 to108, and so must have formed part of a much larger series, and include titles such as 'Widecombe Fair', 'The Seeds of Love', 'Banks of Sweet Primroses', 'High Germany', two versions of both 'John Barleycorn' and' The Derby Ram', as well as 'The Wrestling Match', 'A Cornish Young Man', 'Sheep Shearing Days', 'Watchet Sailor', etc. etc., all good to hear when skillfully sung.

Although he had joined the Torquay Natural History Society in 1917, he probably began to have closer links with it from around 1934, when he inherited Mrs Annie Laycock's house 'Braddonfield', a large house set in gardens which extended from Braddons Hill Road East down to Museum Road, a short distance behind the museum.[26] One reason for this closer connection was that it had recently received 'The Devon Folk-Collection from Farms and Cottages' formed by Mrs Marjory Eckett Fielden largely between 1931 and 1934. During these years she had toured the region on foot and by bus 'to search for surviving instances of ancient usages and customs, and also to collect... old fashioned tools and utensils before all these remnants of Old England are altogether lost' and to 'Log or Record how and where old customs and methods survive on Devonshire today [since] in this age of machinery, motoring and sophisticating wireless, old customs, ancient methods and

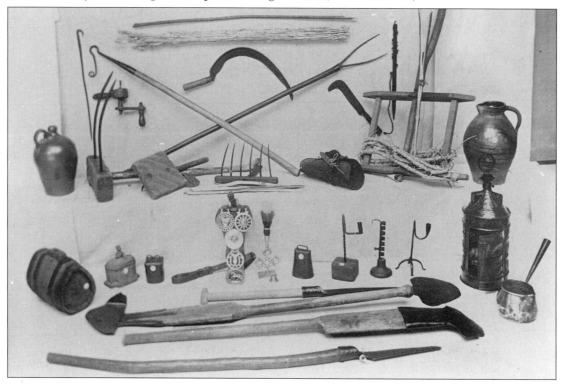

Thatching equipment (top), Dartmoor peat cutting euipment (below), and other farmhouse articles seen here form part of 'The Devon Folk Collection from Farms and Cottages' gathered by Mrs Marjory Fielden between 1931 and 1934.

traditional craftsmanship are disappearing as swiftly and as surely as are the wild flowers and the quiet green lanes with all their wealth of Peace and Beauty'. Her splendid article which records her findings, was printed in the *Transactions of the Devonshire Association* for 1934.

It is not surprising that Mrs Fielden and Charles Laycock soon became close friends, for they shared so much of the same aims and interests. In August 1933, they went to see the village sports at Whiddon Down, noting the throwing rings, races, skittle-throwing for a pig, and the step-dancing of Albert Cocker of South Tawton, an expert performer on the tin whistle for dance tunes. 'The scene presented a true picture of Old English life', she remembered. When Mrs Fielden set up a Devon Kitchen in the museum in 1936 it was Charles Laycock who provided the required funds of £568, a very considerable sum for that period. Further proof of their mutual respect comes from the following poem which Mrs Fielden wrote to Mr Laycock. It is a remarkable piece, redolent of its period, a closely-observed word-picture of Charles Laycock's 'Den' at Moretonhampstead which may have been inspired by the photograph which shows him sitting on the settle.

THE OLD OPEN-HEARTH FIREPLACE

Home come I in the dimpsey, when the work of the day is done,
And all the purple hills are glowing in the light of the setting sun.
Home to the cob-walled cottage with its roof of mellow thatch,
Glad come I to the doorway, and I lift the time-worn latch.
And open the Book of Life at a long-forgotten page,
And enter another region of Beauty and Peace and Age!

My dim old room is lighted by the rushlight's gentle glow,
And softly through the shadows all my dear old treasures show;
On clavey-tack are gleaming all my candlesticks of brass
And little ships in bottles sailing fairy seas of glass,
And there I see the faces of my friendly cloamen dogs,
And here beside the settle are my threshel and my clogs;
With brightly-tinted samplers all my ancient walls are gay,
And Gramfer Clock stands ready to pass the time o'day,
While on the trestle-table here, my pewter tankard waits,
And over on the dresser are my rows of Pewter plates,
And pans and cans and skillets, all in shining metal cast,
Oh! everywhere about me is the spirit of the past!
And by the open fireplace is my chimney-corner seat,
Ah, here are warmth and welcome, and a rest for weary feet!
Amid the leaping shadows I may sit awhile and dream,
And round me in the firelight see the wistful faces gleam
Of all the folk of olden days who sat so long ago
Around my wide old fireplace where the dying embers glow:
And all about my chimney are the things they left behind,
From chimney-crooks are hanging ancient pots of every kind,
Some crocks and three-legged kettles and a fountain of huge size,
And in the cloamen oven there, a salamander lies,

And on the hearth some brandises and brazen trivets stand,
Such simple things, so worn and old, but wrought by Craftsman's hand
In patterns old as time to fill the simple needs of folk
Who lived in peace around my hearth until the Engine woke
Old England to the hum and stir and squalor of Today!
Around the hearth were gathered all their love and work and play.
Why, here they sang their sweet old songs, and told their brave old tales,
And did their work, and cooked their food, and brewed their heather ales.
And I can hear the very heart of Merrie England beat
Within the ancient hearthplace here beside my chimney-seat!

And thus beside my hearth I sit and muse of days of old,
And dream of all their beauty till the moon and stars grow cold,
And cold upon the hearthstone lies the glowing peat at last,
As cold upon Old England lie the ashes of her Past!

From 1936 Charles Laycock began to present various traditional artefacts for display in the museum, and also to make plans for the long-term preservation of his collection by means of a will, dated 10 September 1940. Following his death at 'Braddonfield' on 28 March

This crucifixion group and guillotine from the Laycock collection were carved around 1806-8 by French prisoners of war at Princetown on Dartmoor, using bones saved from the meat rations.

1943, at the age of 63, his body was carried back to Moretonhampstead for burial in the north side of the churchyard, in the beautiful Dartmoor countryside he loved, and with a headstone in the form of a simple Dartmoor granite cross. Now the Torquay Natural History Society found that he had left to its museum all the furniture and other articles at Cross Street, Moretonhampstead such 'as are similar to furniture and articles found in old Devonshire farm houses or cottages', and the sum of £10 000 upon trust to build a room over the museum's Pengelly Hall to house the same, and any additions.

The Trustees were also given £1000 to be invested to produce an income to keep the collection in good order, any surplus to go to the general purposes of the museum, as well as his library of 1700 books, 800 pieces of china and porcelain from 'Braddonfield', and his extremely valuable philatelic collection. The funds generated by his grandfather's long career in industrial Huddersfield were now to ensure that Charles Laycock's Devonshire collections would be permanently preserved and displayed in the Torquay Museum.

According to entries in the museum's accession books, the remainder of his moveable estate, that which had not been left to the museum, was dispersed by sale, cat. no.127, for example, a warming pan, being 'purchased at Laycock sale Moretonhampstead, by Mrs Fielden for £9'.

Due to the great restriction on building materials etc. during the war and immediate post-war period, work on the new gallery had to be delayed until March 1954, when a special meeting agreed the plans, and awarded the contract to Staverton Brothers Ltd. of Totnes. Work started shortly afterwards, and on 28 October 1955, the Laycock Gallery, showing Charles Laycock's collections, was officially opened by Sir George Dyson, KCVO, D.Mus, LLD, Chairman of the Carnegie United Kingdom Trust.[27]

In addition to the Laycock, Fielden, Karkeek and Chope collections, numerous individuals, chiefly members of the Society, have donated hundreds of specimens relating to the traditional life of Devon. Considered as a single entity, they form one of the finest regional collections to be found in any English museum. They clearly illustrate just what can be achieved once the enthusiasm, ability and generosity of private collectors is chanelled through a society, all for the benefit of the general public.

Notes

1. P.Brears 'Bygones in the Connoisseur' *Folk Life* 35 (Leeds 1996) 30-42
2. G. Jekyll *Old West Surrey* (London 1909) viii-ix.
3. see C.S.B. *Handbook of Folklore* The Folklore Society 73 (London 1913)
4. *Journal of the Torquay Natural History Society* 1 (Torquay 1914) 52
5. ibid. 49
6. *Torquay Natural History Society Journal of Transactions and Proceedings* 4 (Oxford 1926) 109 and *Reports and Transactions of the Devonshire Association* 35 (vol 5, second series) (Plymouth 1903) 39
7. Most of his papers were published in *Rep.& Trans. Dev. Assoc.* between 1874 and 1896.
8. *Guide to the Museum* (Torquay 1908) 12
9. *Jnl. Torq. Nat. Hist. Soc.* (see note 4) 52, and H.H.Walker *Torquay Natural History Society, the First Hundred Years 1844-1969* (Torquay 1969) 16
10. *Jnl. Torq. Nat. Hist. Soc.* 2(1915-20) 308 and R.P.Chope 'Some Old Farm Implements and Operations' *Trans. Dev. Assoc.* (Plymouth 1918) 268-92
11. ibid. 250 and *Jnl. Torq. Nat. Hist. Soc.* 3 (1921-22) 59
12. For an extensive biography of J.C. Laycock, see the *Huddersfield Examiner* Sat.21st Feb.,1885,p.8
13. D.F.E.Sykes *History of Huddersfield* (Huddersfield N.D.) 353 and 323
14. eg. *Postal Directory Huddersfield & District* (London 1884) 41. Fitzwilliam St West. J.C.Laycock gentleman, W.Laycock solicitor.
15. eg. Jones' *Directory of Halifax, Huddersfield & Dewsbury* (1863) Laycock & Dyson, St George's Square. Law List (1871)
16. *Slater's Directory*.(1887). W.Laycock, Bryan Lodge, Edgerton
17 For general biographical details, see his obituaries in *The Devonian Year Book* (London 1944) 22-3 and *Trans. Dev. Assoc.* 75 (1943) 1918.
18. *Trans. Dev. Assoc.* 40 (Plymouth 1908) 32
19. ibid. 54 (Plymouth 1923) 255
20. ibid. 229, G.Jekyll (see note 2 above), and A.Hayden *Chats on Cottage and Farm-house Furniture* (London 1912, reprinted 1919)
21. *Trans. Dev. Assoc.* 52 (Plymouth 1920) 158-191; 53 (Plymouth 1923) 224-270, and 55 (Plymouth 124) 154-181
22. These lectures were presented at Torquay Museum on 30/1/1912; 27/12/21 and 11/2/1914
23. Torquay Museum. Letter from W.E.Hall, hon. secretary, to Sara Jackson, librarian to the English Folk Dance and Song Society.
24. As note 22, 15/1/1918 and 16/1/1919
25. Torquay Natural History Society Library Number 92A Reading Room.
26. *Kelly's Directory of Torquay & Paignton* (London 1933) lists Mrs Laycock at 'Braddonfield' and Charles Laycock there in its 1935 edition.
27 H.H.Walker *Torquay Natural History Society... .* (Torquay 1969) 26

KEY

1. Porch
2. Drang-way
3. Front kitchen
4. Back kitchen
5. Backlet
6. Wood-house
7. Cellar
8. Brew-house
9. Pound-house
10. Kitchen garden
11. Backlet and skilling
12. Dairy
13. Cheese room
14. Parlour
15. Dining room
16. Master's bedroom
17. Farm apprentices and servants' bedroom
18. Pigs' houses
19. Calves' houses
20. Root-house
21. Shippens (cow houses)
22. Farm court
23. Barn
24. Round-house with horse wheel.

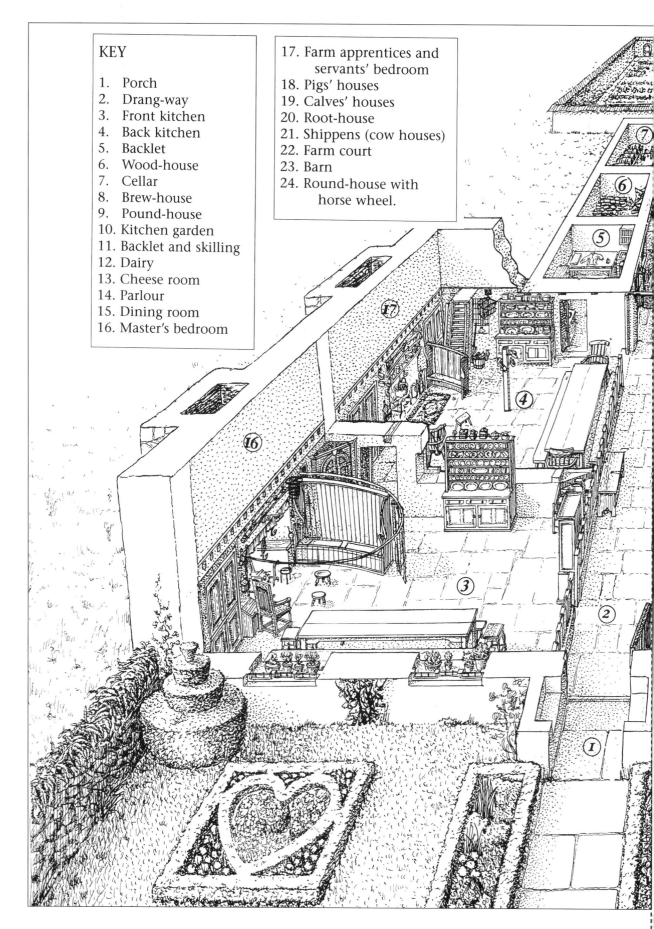

THE DEVON BARTON

This drawing, using Charles Laycock's descriptions, shows the Barton from the south, around 1860.

The barton described by Charles Laycock was demolished around 1900, and remains unidentified. It must have closely resembled Cottles Barton at North Tawton, seen here. The topiary in the garden, the porch, casement windows, thatched gabled dormers and two large rooms to the right are all indenticle to those of the barton he remembered.

NOTE

In the following section words in **bold type** identify, where they first appear, Devon vernacular expressions used for everyday items and places in and around the farmhouse. Numbers in brackets e.g. (323) refer to specific drawings in the catalogue included at the back of the book.

The
Old Devon Farmhouse

In 1920 Charles Laycock began to write a description of a Devon barton. This word, coming from the Old English *bere-tun* or barley enclosure, was used in Devon and Cornwall to describe a large farm occupied either by the owner himself, or by his hind or farm bailiff. The example he had selected had been pulled down some years before, but by enriching his early memories of it with those of elderly people, and actual artefacts collected from it, such as a bench (323), an American clock (377) etc., he was able to re-create it in its mid-Victorian state, 'when all its time honoured articles of furniture, household utensils and cottage ornaments were still to be found in their accustomed places, in which many of them had stood for a couple of centuries or more'. His description, completed three years later, was a masterpiece of informed observation, equal to, if not surpassing, anything which had been attempted in Britain or Europe up to that time.

Taking us by the hand, he conducts us from the lane, across the **homer-field** or meadow to the wicket gate, up the garden path, through the house, and out into the yard, pointing out every item of interest on the way. By combining this wealth of information with the sketch plans and the collections which he left to the Torquay Museum, it has been possible to draw the barton, complete with its interiors etc. with every item precisely as it was around the 1860s (as shown on pages 18 and 19). Using this drawing for reference, we can now begin our own tour of the property, adding the observations of R.P. Chope, Mrs M.E. Fielden and others where appropriate to supplement Charles Laycock's major work.

On opening the wicket gate, a paved or cobbled path extended directly up the front garden towards the porch. To each side, across box-hedged flower beds, were square grass **plats** with round, heart, diamond, star or lovers'-knot **flower-nats** at their centres, each being filled with a selection of the following plants;

Common Name	Latin Name
Bachelor's-buttons	*Ranunculus acris* and *Bellis perennis*
Bloody-warriors	wallflowers, usually the dark red variety
Bloomy-downs	Sweet Williams *Dianthus barbatus*
Bunny-rabbits	Snapdragons *Antirrhinum majus*
Butter-and-eggs	Common Toadflax *Linaria vulgaris* or double daffodil *Narcissus pseudonarcissus*
Clove-jilaufer	Clove Pink *Dianthus caryophyllus*
Duck-bills	*Dielytra spectabilis*
Golden-dust	Yellow Alyssum *Alyssum saxatile*
Grannie's nightcaps	Columbine *Aquilegia*
Money-in-both-pockets or Silks-and-satins	Honesty *Lunaria biennis*
Polyanthums	*Polyanthus*
Racklisses	*Auriculas*
Scarlet-lightnin'	*Lychnis chalcedonia*
Snow-on-the-mountain	White Alyssum *Alyssum maritinum* or *Arabis hirsuta*

In addition to this colourful display, there were peacocks, horses, tables, spinning tops and plumes cut in box, holly, yew or other evergreen topiary, and probably a monkey-puzzle tree. The whitewashed cob frontage of the farmhouse itself supported ivy, Viginia creeper, Wisteria, *Jessamy* (Jasmine), Quincy (Japan Quince *Pyrus japonica*), or Summer-rose (*Kerria japonica* or *Corchorus japonica*) while the massive porch was flanked by honeysuckle to one side, and the sweet Monthly Rose on the other.

The stout oak **vore-door**, two to three inches thick, and sometimes made of two layers of wood clamped together with square or rose-headed nails, swung on a pair of large iron **hangin-crooks** (hinges) driven deeply into the door frame. This structure comprised two upright **durns** (jambs) of almost foot-square oak, with a **lintern** (lintel) across the top, and a narrow two-inch high **drexal**, **drashal** or **druck-stool** (threshold) across the bottom. To gain access, the inner wooden **hapse** (latch) was raised either by inserting a finger through a hole cut through the door just beneath it, or by pulling a cord or leather thong which portruded from a hole bored above it. However, neither of these methods would be effective if the iron bolt had been shot ito its socket, or the detachable wooden bar had been fitted into its iron staple on one side of the doorframe and into its socket cut in the wall opposite, or the key turned in the massive oak-cased lock.

Once the door was opened, it revealed a wide granite-block or stone-flagged **drang-way** or cross-passage, which ran directly through the house to the back door. Its walls were formed from broad oak planks set in deep grooves cut in the sides of thicker uprights, these in turn being set in oaken sills at ground level and beams at ceiling height. Here there was only one piece of furniture, a six-plank **dower-chest** or **linen hutch**, carved or scratch-moulded (335), with an internal **skibbet** or lidded till built

into the top of its right-hand end. By lifting the iron **thumb-latch** and **snite**, or **Norfolk latch** of the first door on the left, we entered the front kitchen, a room where baking and some cooking operations were carried out, but which retained a degree of social prestige since meals were only taken here on Sundays, high days and holidays.

The structure of this room was quite basic, the floor being of well-scrubbed stone flags sprinkled with sand, and with patterns scored with Bath brick around its perimeter. The flags acted as the farmer's barometer, **eaving** or sweating with condensation when wet weather was immenent. At ceiling height, above the roughly-plastered white-washed walls, four adze-hewn dark oak beams ran from front to back, forming a convenient hanging place for dried hams, spare christmas puddings, dried herbs tied in muslin bags, brass and horn lanterns and, at Christmas time, bunches of mistletoe 'vor the bwoys to kiss the maidens under'. Here too hung the **neck**, the miniature sheaf of corn, the very last cut from the previous harvest, so long as the old custom of 'Crying the Neck' was kept up.

The joists which ran from beam to beam were underdrawn with flat panels of white-washed lath and plaster, the space between these and the bedroom floorboards forming a false floor where coinage and valuables might be hidden, certainly from the Civil War period, if not earlier. In the left-hand corner of the fireplace wall, a deep box formed by three planks, one open side and with a slatted wooden floor, was fixed directly beneath the ceiling. This was the bacon-rack, where flitches of home-cured bacon were left to dry, well away from the attentions of rats and cats, while their unbleached calico bags effectively kept the flies at bay.

Proceeding clockwise around the front kitchen from the drang-way door, the first major feature to be seen was the table (327), its well-scrubbed top sitting on a sturdy

trustle or frame. On its window side, just beneath the window ledge bearing the dame's scarlet geraniums, pelargoniums, ferns, parlour palms etc. a plank-topped bench was formed in the thickness of the wall. This provided permanent seating down one side of the table, a loose form (323) being set down the opposite side, and a joined stool (296-299) at each end.

Here the farmer and his family sat at the fireplace end, with the servants, labourers, milk maids, dairy maids and labourers' wives and daughters at the other. Board cloths of handspun and home-woven linen were used only for special occassions, the table usually being left quite bare. Knives (1081-1086) taken from the knife box (347-348) hanging on the wall were then set out with the two- or three-pronged steel forks (1087-1108), the wood, horn, brass or more usual pewter spoons (1109-1110), and the pewter, or perhaps wooden condiments (1053-1065). For the farmer and his family the plates were of pewter (1072-1080), while the servants ate from wooden platters known as **timber-dishes** or **trauncherds** (1066-1070).

Cider and ale were the traditional drinks of Devon. Both were made in the farm yard, where the pound-house provided accommodation for the mill which crushed the apples and the press which extracted the juices which, when fermented, produced both the rough scrumpy and the finest of ciders.

The ale made in the adjacent brew-house still followed the medieval west-country tradition of 'white ale' which, according to local stories, had been introduced either by a seventeenth-century farrier as a drench for sick cows, or by a German surgeon to keep his troops free from the plague.[1] Both of these explanations are quite unfounded, for back in 1542 Andrew Boorde had noted its distinctive characteristics in his *Dyetary of Helth*:

'I am a Cornish man, ale I can brew;
It will make one to kack, also to spew.
It is so thick and smoky, and also it is thin,
It is like wash, that pigs had wrestled therein.'

Dr Karkeek found that it was still being made in the South Hams of Devon in the 1870s, and was able to collect detailed instructions for its production. In appearance, it was not unlike very milky tea, having considerable quantities of some white substance floating about in it, which had a tendency to settle at the bottom of the glass. 'It is so thick', he wrote, 'that the *habitues...* have a peculiar knack of placing the little finger of the left hand under the cup and give it a rolling motion from the left to the right, as they raise it to their lips, in order to prevent a settlement from taking place in the glass'.

Truly this was a very *real* ale, being appreciated both as a cold drink for summer and as a hot drink for winter, when it was heated in copper mullers specially designed either as cones to thrust down into a fire burning in a range (1040-1044), or as a long slipper shape to slip beneath the peat or wood embers of the down-hearth (1045-1047). Both cider and ale were brought to the table either in pewter **vlagins** or flagons, frequently engraved with a name or the initials and a date, or in large black leather jugs or bombards (1114-1121). From these, the liquor was poured either into horn mugs (1186-1182), individual pewter **tankets** or tankards (1170-1174), wooden tankards (1175), or leather black-jacks (1165-1169), quarts and pints for the men, and half-pints for the women.

From the middle of the nineteenth century these customs and utensils began to undergo a period of considerable change. Probably as a combined result of the education of the labourers, the increasing 'gentility' of the farmers, and the social values they absorbed from the London and other

urban visitors to whom they rented their homes during the agricultural depression, the farmers and labourers ceased to share the same table.

In the front kitchen, the old joint stools were replaced by windsor chairs (314-318), tablecloths came into general use, and pewter and wooden tableware was replaced by the best **chiney** service probably of Staffordshire manufacture. Since many of the once-prized pewter plates were now consigned to the labourers in the harvest field, or feeding dogs and chickens in the yard, only the best were **shined up** for display on the dresser.[2] Since the timber dishes were less durable, and could help to fuel the fire, most disappeared, although one round example was retained for the old Christmas game of 'turning the traunchard'. Pewter and leather were similarly replaced by pottery vessels for serving the beer and cider, ceramic jugs and mugs now coming in many shapes and designs, decorated with lustre, transfer and enamel colours (1131-1136 & 1183-1187). Glass mugs, and later thick glass tumblers, were also introduced during this period of change.

Continuing beyond the table, the left end of the fireplace wall was occupied by a deep, double-doored cupboard, hollowed out from the thickness of the cob wall. Here all the family's groceries were kept dry by the adjacent fire, as was the flour-hutch and the leather-hinged salt-box hanging on the wall above (344-346). Nearby stood the master's chair, usually a straight-backed seventeenth century armchair where 'the good farmer takes his Sunday afternoon **zog**, and his well-earned "night-cap" before **gwain up timbern 'eel** (the timber hill, or staircase) to bed. On winter nights this would be a very snug and **lew** (sheltered) seat, especially when the curtain which ran along the semi-circular iron hoop suspended from the ceiling and the fireplace wall was pulled close, forming a warm room within a room.

Inside this area, at the opposite side of the fireplace, stood the settle, its curved back following the line of the encircling curtain, staight settles being virtually unknown in Devon. In this particular front kitchen, the settle was plank-built in oak, with lids set into the boxed-in seat giving access to storage space for anything which had to be kept dry (326). This space could also serve as a safe and effective cradle for the baby when its mother was working at the fire. Further storage was provided within the tall back of the settle, two folding doors opening at the rear so that flitches of bacon could be hung from a row of strong iron hooks within. At other farmhouses the settles might be anything from 3ft 6ins to over 8ft in length, of planked or framed construction, in oak or elm. There might be double doors opening to the front (325), or perhaps two long narrow cupboards for small groceries etc. mounted along the top front edge. In exceptional circumstances, large settles at each side of the fire could be drawn together and securely hooked up to each other in this position to form a continuous semicircular seat and an ideal draughtproof screen around the fire.

Two or three three-legged **cricket** stools (304-6) provided seating for children and for cats to **croodle auver the vire**, with four-legged rectangular footstools (300-303) for the comfort of the adults. There were also **chimley-cornder saits** to each side of the actual fire, these either being built of stone, frequently with wooden plank tops, or else taking the form of rectangular wooden stools (294). Here 'dear old Gramfer was wont to sit during the cold winter evenings, smoking his long clay pipe, drinking his **tanket o'cider** and delighting in a tale about the **gude old taimes** in the days of his youth; while Grannie on the opposite seat would nod assent to every remark he made, and gradually fall asleep over her knitting, as the dying embers glowed and crickets chirruped merrily on the hearth'.

This Devonshire fireplace, lit with a fire-window on the left, shows how the hearth could be built up with bricks to form a convenient pit for the fire. In the centre an iron kettle hangs from the 'chimley bar' fixed across the inside of the chimney.

As for the fireplace itself, its wide rectangular opening was bridged by a huge oak or elm **clavel** or lintel measuring anything from 1ft. 6ins to 3ft in thickness. Along its inner edge nails and hooks supported hams or sides of bacon while they dried and cured, but its most conspicuous feature was the **clavey-tack** or mantlepiece, mounted on brackets half-way up its front face. This held a variety of articles, both useful and ornamental, including a pair of brass candlesticks (235-251), one at either end, shined up for decoration once their practical role had been superceded by oil lamps or gaslights. There were also sheet iron candlesticks (230-234), whose bases provided an ideal edge to scrape the outer skin and bristles off freshly-scalded slaughtered pigs, the hairs still being found inside the stems of some examples. There were tinder boxes for making light and fire (143-153), rush-light holders, designed to gently hold peeled lengths of the common rush *Juncus conglomeratus* which had been dipped in tal-

low melted in a **grisset pan** (167-169), and snuffers (178-186) in their trays (187-189) used for trimming straight lengths of burnt-out wick from the old dipped or moulded (170-171) tallow candles to stop them smoking and control the flame in the days before modern wicks, which automatically bend sideways to be consumed in the side of the flame. There were brass flour dredgers for frothing the spit-roast meat (735-737), tobacco boxes (1188-1193), a copper **biggin** or coffee pot (1150), sugar cutters (674-682), and the old brass pestle and mortar (689-710), still retained for tinkling like a bell to encourage swarming bees to settle. Lastly, there were the Staffordshire pottery figures, such as a pair of **cloam** or chiney dogs (518-561), Dick Turpin and Tom King (461-463), Little Red Riding Hood (471) etc. referred to by the farmer's wife as her **joanies**.

Further items hung from the walls to each side of the fireplace, these included a candle box (172-177), two brass ladles formerly used for basting the meat (884-892), a brass

toasting fork (cf 831-833), a brass **raimer** or skimmer (958-964), a brass chestnut roaster (904-905), ale and cider warmers (1040-1047), and a warming pan (127-133). This last item was filled with glowing embers from the hearth just before the family retired to bed, the mistress then running it up and down between the sheets in each bed to ensure that it was aired and warm. This was a skillful business, for the sheets were easily scorched if the pan was not kept constantly on the move. A safer alternative was to use one of the water-filled warming pans (134-135), or oval bed warmers (136), but these were all superceded from the mid nineteenth century when **cloamen** (pottery) hot water bottles and jars, and later rubber hot water bags, came into general use.

In many farmhouses the hearth was at floor level, being made of stone blocks, or of narrow stone slabs set closely on edge to form a heat-resistant surface. Alternatively the hearth could be made of bricks laid one or two layers above floor level, and having either a flat surface for the fire to burn on, or a central rectangular recess, one brick deep, in which the fire could burn tidily, without scattering its embers. In the in-country the hedges and copses provided an abundance of firewood which could be burned on the bare hearth, with just a pair of **vire dogs** or larger **andirons** (92-100 and 852-859) to raise the ends of the logs, preventing them from **vallin' abroad** and introducing a little draught so that they might burn clearly. On the moorland borders **turf**, the peat, and **vags**, the surface parings, as well as wood, were burned, while farmers in the heart of the moors burned just turf and vags, which they could cut solely for their own use as part of their Venville Rights. These rights, based on the *'fines villarum'* (corrupted to *fin-vil*, then *venville*) paid to the Duchy of Cornwall, were of great antiquity, one Walter Bradmore being fined for digging turfs and selling them without license from the Lidford Manor Court in 1468.[3] Usually they were also burned directly on the hearth, but raised hearths formed from closely-spaced iron bars (82) enabled them to burn more brightly, a similar solution being adapted in the early nineteenth century turf-plates of the North York Moors.[4] No fenders were ever used, but the back of the fire might be protected from the heat of the flames and the bruising of the logs by fairly plain arch-topped firebacks (85), the more ornamental varieties only being used in more prestigious fireplaces.

To **teen** or kindle the fire, a **yaffle o'facket 'ood** (handfull of dry sticks), a **blast o' vuzz** (brand of dried gorse), or a **vew cricks** (bundle of dried hedge-clippings) was placed across the firedogs and lit using the tinder box. This was traditionally a wooden box with two compartments (145-146), that nearest to the handle holding a steel striker (139-142) and a piece of flint, while the other held the tinder itself (a kind of linen 'charcoal' made by charring pieces of cloth to blackness) beneath a flat wooden damper. Taking the flint in one hand, and the steel in the other, sparks were struck on to the tinder, starting a red glow which, when placed in a small mound of fine kindling and blown gently, soon sprang into flame. This process was made much simpler if a match made of a thin strip of wood, its ends cut to a point and dipped in sulphur, was touched on to the glowing tinder, which resulted in an instant, flaring flame. Some pocket tinder boxes held a flint, a steel, and a piece of tinder (147), or incorporated steels within their structure (143-144), while larger ones for kitchen use could contain both sulphur matches and a piece of candle, either to retain the flame, or for illumination (148-153). In the mid eighteenth century flintlock tinderboxes or strike-a-lights which used a mechanism similar to that of a flintlock pistol, were available for wealthier households (154-155).

Chemical methods of making fire were introduced in the early nineteenth century in the form of the 'Instantaneous Light Box' (157). This contained matches dipped in potassium chlorate and sugar, and a small bottle of sulphuric acid, which caused the matches to flame furiously and so be used to light a short candle held in a small hinged holder. Lucifer matches, ignited by friction, were first introduced into North Devon by pedlars in 1842, but tinder boxes remained in regular use certainly up to the 1880s, and came back into use in 1918 when matches became unavailable in country places. Mr Pedick of Braunton made cow-horn tinder boxes for local soldiers at this time, while at Moretonhampstead, Charles Laycock found a local labourer using tinder he had made by soaking a piece of thick brown paper into a solution of saltpetre and gently drying it in the oven: 'His method was to wrap a piece of tinder around the back of his large pocket knife, leaving a small portion of the steel exposed. He held this in his left hand, while he struck the flint against the steel with his right hand, when, usually after two or three strokes, the sparks would set the tinder alight, and so he was enabled to light his pipe straight from the burning tinder. And the stronger the wind, the more brightly the tinder would burn'.[5]

To encourage the fire on the hearth to catch light and burn efficiently, both the traditional form of **bellises** or bellows were used (101-103), as well as an interesting range of home-made centrifugal wheel bellows (105-108).

To manage the fire, individual logs or turves were moved around the fire as they burned using either log forks (109-113) or **vire-tongs**, or **tongses** of a distinctive regional form, with a small terminal knob and a hinge half-way up the elongated head (117-118); described in the old riddle:

'Long legs, crooked thighs,
Little 'aid, an no eyes'.

Neither pokers (114-115) nor shovels were very common except where coal was burned as a fairly recent innovation.

For cooking over the fire, a great variety of supports were required. About 8ft above the hearth a stout iron bar ran from one side of the chimney flue across to the other, this being known as the **chimley-bar** or **back-bar**. In some districts it was made of wood, usually chestnut, the hardness of the wood and its height above the fire apparently preventing it from catching alight.

At least three or four **chimley-crooks** (761-779) working on the rack-and-hook principle were hung from this bar so that any vessel hooked on to their lower ends could be moved up and down, or from side to side if the crook was slid along the bar.

Among the other items to be hooked on to the crooks were extension hooks (780-784), kettle-tilters or idle-backs (785-788), pot-hangers (791-793) which fitted into the side loops of **crocks** or cauldrons etc., and **bearers** (794-795) which supported frying pans etc. over the fire.

In contrast to the northern and eastern parts of England, chimney cranes (796-797) were quite unusual in Devon, only being found in the largest farmhouses and country mansions, and even there they were relatively plain and simple in their design. Very short chimney crooks were specially made to accompany them (777-778).

When the fire was low, the cooking vessels were placed on strongly made iron stands, through-rivetted and with fire-welded joints to withstand the heat. These **brandises** or **brandires** were mostly round in plan (744-760), as described in the riddle:

'So round's a 'oop, so black's a craw
Dree legs, an' a dumpin 'aul'
(So round as a hoop, so black as a crow,
Three legs, and a thumping hole)

Triangular brandises were also common (742-743), the expression brandis-wise or

brandis-fashion being used to describe anything triangular, as in the three roads at Brandis Corner in North Devon and at Brandish Street at Allerford, between Minehead and Porlock. Larger rectangular brandises were made too (738 & 741), as well as rectangular brandis-like frames, but without legs (739-740), which probably stood on bricks, stones, or perhaps the horizontal bars of the fire dogs when cooking over the embers.

On 27 February 1802, George Bodley of Exeter patented the first practical closed-fire iron cooking range, which heated a hotplate top, an oven and a water boiler, all from the same fire.[6] Its use was probably restricted to the urban coal-burning households up to the mid nineteenth century, when they began to be installed in the larger farmhouse kitchens.

For these, and for simpler ranges with open firebars, both in the kitchen and in the parlour, a further series of supports were required. The most practical of these, used for actual cooking, were the **brigs** which spanned the space between the top firebar and the fireback (798).

In contrast, **trivets** were designed to stand before the fire to keep food warm, rather than within it for cooking. Since they could be used in the parlour too, they were lighter in construction, and might include polished brass, wood and pottery details within their construction. Some were circular (799-800), incorporating plate tilters (801) or toasting forks (802). Others had both three legs to stand on the hearth and hooks to fit on to the firebars (803-806), while a further group had only the hooks (809-817).

Larger iron or brass trivets, rectangular in plan and with elaborate 'cabriole' front legs, generally known as 'footmen' in other parts of England, were widely used too (818-824), their broad tops enabling kettles, saucepans and dripping pans to be kept piping hot in front of the fire.

For keeping individual plates of food warm, especially the hot toast, muffins etc. which had just been taken from the toasting forks, six-legged **cats** were placed near the fire (825-830). Like their feline namesakes, they always landed on their feet, but unlike any real cat, they always left three legs up in the air to support a plate and its contents at any desired angle towards the radiant heat.

When meat was to be roasted, a pair of large **andires** (852-859) was arranged with one to each side of the hearth, the uprights bearing a series of hooks which supported the spits horizontally in front of the fire. Most spits were simple rectangular bars, forged round at both ends, with sliding forks to grip the meat, and a handle by which they were slowly rotated, ensuring that the joint gradually absorbed the radiant heat, until it was 'done to a turn' (841-845).

The problem with the hand-turned spits was the great amount of uncomfortable, hot, tedious and time-consuming labour involved in their use. By the late sixteenth century at least, weight-driven clockwork mechanisms called jacks had been introduced for this purpose, these being screwed to one end of the clavel, from where a loop of rope or chain dangled down to support and rotate a grooved wood or iron pulley wheel fixed to one end of the spit (846-849). From the fifteenth century, or earlier, the energy created by the rush of hot air and smoke up the chimney had also been used to operate propeller blades and gearing to turn roasting spits. By the mid eighteenth century many kitchen chimneys were being reduced to form a large circular flue just below ceiling height, a large vane or propeller mounted here being rapidly spun round by the draught, this movement then driving a shaft which passed through the chimney breast to a pulley for the spit chain (865). Being expensive, their use was restricted to the largest farms, manor houses and mansions, most modest establishments relying on the cheaper, but still practical and

This remarkable illustration, taken from a contemporary photogaph, shows dinner being cooked for farmer T. Endacot's family at Wingstone, Manaton, in 1927. With the huge fountain hanging on the left, the row of pans on the 'brandis', the kettle on its 'chimley crook', the 'baker' or camp kettle heated by the fire below and by glowing embers piled on its lid, and the plates and tureens warming on the hearth, it clearly shows how the open fire could be used to produce excellent meals.

convenient bottle-jack (866-870). Invented in the late eighteenth century, this device had a broad cylindrical barrel containing a spring-driven clockwork motor hung vertically from a narrower tubular neck to produce a bottle-shaped body, sheathed either in sheet brass or stove-enamelled tin-plate. When hung from a bracket (876-879) screwed on to the **clavel**, and wound up, it remained quite stationary, but once the combined weight of an iron flywheel (870-874), a meat hook (875), and a joint of meat was loaded on to the hook portruding from its base, it gradually rotated them a number of turns in one direction, then gave a pronounced click before going into reverse for a similar number of turns, continuing in this way for perhaps half an hour or more before rewinding was required.

Whichever type of jack was used, the juices flowing from the roasting meat were caught in a dripping pan, probably a small square example standing on a brandis or trivet beneath (882). Larger dripping pans, perhaps some three feet in length, could incorporate their own legs and provide support for a **saver**, a three-inch high strip of sheet iron mounted on small feet at the front of the dripping pan to stop the ashes and embers from falling into the dripping. A three-fold galvanised sheet iron **sconce** was then placed behind the meat, to reflect and contain the heat radiating from the fire, and to protect the joint from the cold draught which the fire constantly drew from the kitchen, and up the chimney.

To keep the meat moist, its juices were regularly scooped up from the dripping pan

and poured over the joint using a basting spoon (885-890), the finer examples incorporating a strainer to catch any bits of ash etc. which might otherwise stick to the surface of the meat and spoil its flavour.

Shortly before serving, a flour dredger (835-837) was taken from the mantlepiece and its contents sprinkled over the freshly basted meat, thus building up a crisp, flavoursome 'froth', one of the great delicacies of the spit-roasted joint. By the mid nineteenth century these rather messy procedures were greatly improved by the use of specially-designed hasteners or Dutch ovens (881). These incorporated a bracket for hanging the bottle jack, a convex shield and reflector of shiny tinplate to concentrate the radiant heat on to the joint, and an integral dripping pan with a central well, fitted with a hinged cover to prevent the embers and coagulated meat juices from contaminating the dripping.

Some manufacturers went on to produce spring jacks and hasteners designed as a single unit to operate horizontal spits, as in 'Pearse's Patent Veruvolver Economical Roasting Apparatus' (850 & 880). This pompous title, derived from the Latin *verus*, a spit, was presumably intended to impress the classically-educated Regency gentry who would be its most probable purchasers. A similar mechanism had a windmill-like spring jack with a horizontal shaft which both turned a spit, and scooped up the dripping so that the meat was automatically basted too (893).

When food was to be broiled, or grilled, over a clear, bright fire, rather than being roasted in front of it, a variety of **gridires** or gridirons was used, these being stood on top of a convenient brandis until their steaks, chops or fish were cooked to perfection. Most examples were simple grids of horizontal bars (894-896,898 & 900) but some local examples had rotating grids (899). The commercially manufactured variety, meanwhile, had gutter-shaped bars which

drained all the juices down into a reservoir near the handle, thus saving the dripping, rather than leaving it to drop into the fire and send up plumes of smoke and ash to spoil the meat (897). Where a fierce top heat was required, which browned the food without cooking it through, as when making burnt cream, or creme brulée, a poker called a salamander (837-839) had its large, thick iron head thrust into the fire until it was red hot. It was then held over the food for only the briefest moment, since it was far hotter than any modern grill, to achieve the desired results. Since this device was only used in high-class cookery, it must always have been extremely rare in Devon farm kitchens.

For frying, the traditional down-hearth frying pans (906-907) had very long iron handles, so that they could be easily managed by someone sitting by the fire, as the bacon, ham and eggs sizzled in their broad pans. Those with shorter handles were ideal for standing on a brandis or bearer over the fire (908 & 911), and the smallest for cooking on the flat top of a Bodley range (909-910). From the mid nineteenth century cast-iron frying pans suitable for either standing on the brandis, hanging from the chimney crook, or using on top of the range began to be introduced into Devon by various manufacturers from the West Midlands (912).

For baking, most houses had an oven built into one corner of the fireplace, usually, but not exclusively, opposite the window, to take advantage of the light. The oven itself took the form of a roughly rectangular or arch-topped doorway leading into a round domed chamber, perhaps up to four feet deep, built into the thickness of the chimney stack. It might be lined with stone on Dartmoor, often with brick in other areas, while to the north and west of the county cloam (pottery) ovens were more common. Made from clay tempered with coarse grit from the river Torridge at

Bideford and made in the North Devon potteries, or perhaps from Lake's Pottery at Truro, these came as ready-made units for building into the masonry. As 'a Gentleman' described in his *Essays for the Month of December* of 1716:

'The Barnstaple Ovens of Devonshire, which are now made and us'd in some other counties; and first being form'd in Potters Clay in one entire Piece, are not only cleaner and cheaper Than any other Ovens, but bake with more Evenness,and Certainty, and consume not a Fourth of the Fuel,which is wasted in those of the ordinary Fashion in London and elsewhere.'

In use, a **facket o' 'ood** (faggot of wood), a **blast o' vuzz** (blast of furze, i.e gorse) ,or, on moorland farms, **turves** (peat), was set alight and thrust into the back of the oven using a furse fork (968-970). As the fuel burned, its smoke issued from the oven door and was drawn up the chimney. Once the oven was really hot, the ashes were pulled out with a rake (116), the fine ash mopped up with a wet oven swab or **mawkin**, and the bread etc. placed inside using a large oven-slice or peel (971-972). The oven door, traditionally a loose slab of wood, usually chestnut, fitted with a handle, or a cloam door (966-967) for a cloam oven, was then placed across the doorway and sealed in place with clay, cob or mortar, but more recent ovens had hinged iron doors, similar to those on industrially-produced kitchen ranges. After perhaps 60 or 70 minutes the baking was complete and, on opening the door, it was drawn out on the peel, and set aside to cool.

As in most parts of upland Britain, there were practical alternatives to heating these large built-in ovens. In Devon, baking on the actual hearth was carried out using a baking kettle, called a **wovering pan** in West Devon. This involved heating a baking iron (973-975), a heavy iron disc, by slipping it under the burning fire. It was then pulled to the side of the hearth, the loaf, cake, or dish of meat and vegetables to be baked placed upon it, and the baking kettle, a three-legged iron pot (976-978), inverted over it. Smouldering turves, **fags** (surface peats), cinders, ashes, **vearns** (bracken), leaves, hay, or even **dowst** (chaff) were then heaped around the kettle, and the whole left to bake slowly for several hours.

In 1750 Dr Richard Pococke had noted that 'in the very western parts they have pot-ovens, a round piece of iron is heated on which the bread is put and is then cover'd over with a pot, on which they heap the embers to keep in the heat'. These pots, or baking kettles, remained in use up to the 1930s, when an old lady at a Poundsgate cottage told Mrs Fielden 'I be gwain to put a' old hen under thic kettle, an' when 'er comes out 'er'll be as tender as a chick!'

Another option was to put the hot baking iron on a very low brandis (752) in the fire on the hearth, place the food on the top, and then cover it with a **baker**, a vessel like a deep iron frying pan but without the long handle. After being covered with burning fuel, it was left to cook. This method, identical to the *padell r gradell* (pan and griddle) baking of the Lleyn peninsular in North Wales, was still being carried out at Poundsgate in the 1930s.

A further method involved the use of a camp kettle, a broad cylindrical iron pot with three short legs, a hoop handle, a slightly domed lid with a raised rim, and an internal false bottom to prevent the food from burning (979). In use, this was either stood in the fire, or hung from a hook over the fire, burning fuel being piled on top of the lid to produce a relatively even all-round heat. These ovens were introduced into most parts of upland Britain in the early nineteenth century, being known as *ffrwn fach* (little ovens) or *crochan pobi* (baking pots) in Wales, or as *yetlings* on the North

York Moors. They were rapidly falling out of use in the 1930s, but Mrs Fielden discovered that they could still be obtained in Devon at that time, if ordered from the Carron foundry at Falkirk in Scotland.

Finally, girdle cakes etc. could be baked on a simple flat round iron plate hung over the fire by means of a bow handle hooked on to one of the chimley hooks, but regrettably Charles Laycock never published his proposed paper on traditional baking and brewing methods, and so detailed information is now no longer available.

Kettles of different shapes and sizes were met with in different Devon farmhouses, the most distinctive being the Dartmoor kettle (1031-1035) with its brass handle and finely-shaped copper body. It was ideal for hanging from the idle-back or kettle tilter (785-788) or standing on a brandis over the fire whenever small quantities of boiling water were required for making tea etc. for those sitting at the nearby table.

Later kettles were made from cast iron in the factories of the West Midlands (1038-1039).

The tour of the front kitchen can now continue from the hearth, around the back of the settle, to where a small cupboard in the wall held any small articles which might be needed by the family. Next to it, the oak corner cupboard (e.g.332) held the dame's pots of home-made preserves, and her bottles of home-made cordials such as metheglin, ginger wine, elderberry wine etc, which provided hospitality before the days of universal tea-drinking.

Many of these bottles had been made locally in the glass kilns at Countess Wear, Topsham, which had been founded before 1702, when they were advertised in the *London Gazette* (22 June, p.112). Some had applied glass seals bearing the names of their owners, such as 'Thomas Smith 1716', 'In. Sandford 1725', 'I.Skinner 1736', 'Richd. Rendall Topsham 1741', 'Chas. Walley

Exmouth 1770', 'S. Pearse Cradleigh 1790' or 'P. Soper'.

'I.Dally E[sq] Thorvertn. 1770' (1001) probably originated here too. Once the home-made or imported liquors had been poured into each bottle, using a pewter funnel (1013-1014), the bottle was placed in a bottle boot (1015) strapped to the thigh, thus holding it safe and firm while the cork, softened in a cork press (1016) was driven securely home using a round wooden driver and a mallet.

Passing round to the north wall, the chief item of furniture was an oak dresser. On its top shelf, all brightly polished, stood what remained of the old pewter plates, tankards and measures, the latter often of copper, left by previous generations. The lower shelves housed the best modern chiney service for use on Sundays and special occassions, the smaller jugs, mugs and cups being hung from iron hooks driven into the front of each shelf. Larger teapots, jugs, a set of old wooden dry-measures, an old wooden coffee mill (1022-1023), spice box (251) and tea caddy (e.g.357-363) etc. all stood ready for use on the flat top of the portruding lower section. Then, in the right-hand corner of the room, encased in broad elm planks, was the 'timbern hill' or staircase leading up to the **chimber** or bedroom above. The **cubby-hole** beneath it had a separate door and provided a useful area in which to store brooms, besoms, buckets, polishing materials etc., and sometimes small supplies of logs and peat for firing.

Nearby, against the eastern wall which backed on to the drang-way or cross-passage, stood the old thirty-hour or long-sleeve clock (374) with its brass dial and polished oak case. The master's last task every night, after taking off his boots, was to wind this clock by pulling up the weight on its chain, rather than use a key. Next to it stood a cupboard-dresser which had its upper shelves enclosed by wood-panelled or

glazed doors, which kept the crockery within clean and free from dust. Having completed the tour of the front kitchen, we can now return into the drang-way, and walk down to the next door on the left, descending a couple of steps into the back kitchen, where food was prepared, cooked and, only on weekdays, eaten.

This room was similar in size to the front kitchen, and had a similar stone-slabbed floor, but its ceiling was completely open, its beams, joists and wide elm floorboards all being exposed to view. These provided extensive storage areas for all manner of tools and equipment, one main beam having iron crooks driven into its sides to support lanterns, saws, hammers, cleavers or bill-hooks, hatchets, scythes, **browse-** or **parin'-hooks** for hedging, dibbers for sowing wheat etc., **picks** (hay forks), reap hooks for harvesting, along with flails and **cider-virkins** (1137-1143).

Another beam supported spare harness and plough tackle, horse brasses on their leathers, spare straw bee-butts, numerous baskets, a **wink** for making straw rope, **want-snaps** (mole traps), rabbit gins, **daggin' shears** (sheep-shears) and steelyards for weighing. The beam near the window also supported a wicker birdcage (384) with a tame cock blackbird, a nail outside the **back-'ouze** door showing where it was hung outside on fine sunny days.

Further items, such as oil cans, bottles of linseed oil, liniment, blue-stone, animal medicines, and wooden spiggots for tapping casks of beer and cider were also stored here on racks made by nailing narrow laths to the joists about an inch appart.

Near the centre of the ceiling one of the main beams was supported by a massive square oak post. This also provided useful storage space, for here the farm labourers used to hitch their hats and caps on to the many nails driven into its sides as they came in for their meals.

Turning left at the doorway, and proceeding clockwise around the back kitchen, the first major feature was a long table with a bench fixed to the drang-way wall along one side, and a moveable one on the other, with a windsor chair set at each end. Here the farmer and his family, and the servants, sat at opposite ends to take their weekday meals. Here too all the food was prepared, much of it being simple but substantial and well-flavoured, as may be seen in the following examples:

Devonshire Stew[7]

1 lb (450g) potatoes, boiled 20 minutes
8 oz. (225g) cabbage, boiled 15
*   minutes*
8 oz. (225g) onions peeled and boiled
*   30 minutes*
Butter or beef dripping. Salt and pepper

1. drain the vegetables, shred them, mix them together, and season with salt and pepper
2. fry in the butter or beef dripping, stirring and shaking the pan to prevent it sticking, until it is golden brown.

Pies were particularly popular, especially squab pie and the doucet pie, for which the following recipe was collected by Mr Chope from the cook of the Royal Hotel in Bideford. The famous 'Tad-a-liv'-'tood-a-gon Pie' was similarly made, but its main ingredient was miscarried piglets.

Squab Pie

2 lb (900g) lamb chops
2 lb (900g) apples
1.5 lb (675g) onions
salt and ground black pepper

Pastry
8 oz (225g) plain flour
4 oz (100g) lard

3-4 tbs (45-60 ml) water
pinch of salt

*1. make the pastry by rubbing the lard into
the flour and salt, mix in the water with a
round-bladed knife to form a dough, and
knead lightly*
*2. trim the fat and bone off the chops, beat
them flat, and season them with the salt
and pepper.*
*3. peel, core and slice the apples, and peel
and slice the onions.*
*4. arrange half the lamb in the bottom of
a large pie dish, cover it with half the
apples, then half the onions, and repeat
these layers to fill the dish.*
*5. roll out the pastry into a large round,
wet the edges of the pie dish, cover it with
the pastry, trim the edges, using the trim-
mings to form a ring around a vent-hole
cut in the centre, and any decorations etc.*
*6. bake at 180°C (350°F) Gas mark 4 for
one and a half hours.*

DOUCET PIE

1.5lb (675g) lean pork, sliced
2 lb (900g) apples, peeled and sliced
8 oz (225g) onions, peeled & sliced
4 oz (100g) stoned raisins
1 tsp (5ml) chopped fresh parsley
half tsp (2.5ml) ground nutmeg or allspice
Proceed as for Squab Pie.

The south wall of the back kitchen was quite
plain, except for the door and former
window which both opened into the front
kitchen, and for an American clock (377)
fixed to the wall by brackets.

The west, or fireplace, wall started with a
deep cupboard hollowed out of the cob,
where boots, leggings and **gambadoes**
(wood-soled leather over-boots to protect
the legs of riders) were all stored. Next came
the fireplace itself, similar to that in the
front kitchen, but two feet narrower, having
neither an oven nor chimney corner seats.

Here most of the larger cooking vessels
and boilers were hung, ranging from the
large dish kettle (1449) in which milk was
warmed for cheesemaking and the family's
washing was boiled, to the iron crocks (919-
922) for boiling potatoes for the pigs, and
warming scald-milk for the calves, as well as
cooking many other foods for human
consumption. Here too hung the large cast-
iron fountain (1028-1030), introduced from
the West Midland manufacturers in the mid
nineteenth century, which provided a ready
supply of boiling water. About the same
time the Bodley ranges with their enclosed
firebox, oven, hotplate and water boiler
began to be installed in one side of the wide
back kitchen fireplaces, enabling baking,
cooking and water heating to be carried out
much more efficiently than before.
However, this still left half or two-thirds of
the hearth to be used in the traditional
manner, an important consideration when
the stove relied on expensive coal and
wood, while the hearth burned the turves
and vags which could be had simply for the
trouble of digging them from the moors.

Above the fireplace the clavey-tack held a
varity of useful items, including tins for
storage, two or three flat irons (630-640),
iron or tin flour or pepper dredgers, a coffee
mill (1022-1023) and spice box (351), and a
couple of old iron candlesticks (230-232),
but none of the brassware or china ornaments found in the front kitchen. On the
wall above the clavey tack a wooden rack
supported the farmer's guns, a blunderbuss,
and their powder and shot flasks, together
with the rattles and bird-clappers (1338-9)
used to scare birds away from the newly-
sown fields.

By the side of the fireplace a simple
plank-built elm settle (324) had various
brown pottery jars, pitchers, bottles (127-
129) etc. tucked in beneath its seat. Here
the dame and her maids sat to pluck the
fowls, and the geese at Michaelmas and
Christmas, keeping the soft, downy feathers

In the Dartmoor cottage seen here, a coal-burning Bodley range has been installed in the left side of the hearth leaving the open fire with its fire dogs and Dartmoor kettle to the right where they continue to be used in the traditional manner, taking advantage of local wood and peat.

for making feather beds. Then, beyond the right-hand end of the fireplace, a straight, steep and narrow flight of open steps led up to the first floor chamber occupied by the young farm labourers and apprentices who lived in. In the space beneath and behind the steps the bucket (286-292) and heath or birch broom used for cleaning the floors were stored, along with the beetle and wedges used for splitting the **brauns** (logs) for firewood.

Nearby, on the window ledge on the north wall, stood a simple barometer made by inverting a salad-oil bottle (1009) into a pickle-jar half full of water, the water being drawn up its neck in fine dry weather, only to recede when wet weather returned. Here too was a glass fly-catcher (664) which used beer or a similar syrupy liquid in its upturned rim to attract and then entrap troublesome flies and wasps during the hot months of summer. Further along the wall

an elm dresser housed the old Asiatic Pheasant pattern blue transfer-printed pottery dinner service, the white and gold teacups, and the mugs in everyday use, thus completing the furnishing of this room.

Next to the dresser, a door led through the north wall into the back-'ouze or **slee**, the true scullery of the farmhouse, where all the cooking utensils and tableware were washed and scoured in a deep stone sink-trough or **zinc-traw**. An iron pump at its side provided a ready supply of cold water, while a slatted wooden dish-rack above held the crockery as it drained after rinsing. Once Bodley ranges began to be fitted in back kitchens, this room was adapted to serve as a wash-house too. A furnace or boiling copper was built into one corner, and a roller mangle, perhaps timber-framed with either granite-weighted levers or springs to provide the pressure, stood alongside, and a

large table installed for folding and ironing the clothes.

Simple flat irons heated on a trivet before the fire, or on the top of the Bodley, were perhaps most common (630-631), the more expensive box irons (633-640) having iron *slugs* or *yetters* which were heated in the fire itself before being slipped inside the body of the iron. Much rarer were the cast brass irons (632), probably of continental origin, which had embers or charcoal glowing within their hollow bodies. For starched ruffles and ribbons, tubular Italian irons (645-656) mounted on heavy bases and heated by their own poker-like slugs (650 & 652) were available, while for convex items, such as the crowns of linen bonnets or perhaps puffed sleeves, there were lump-heads (657). During the mid Victorian period, when it was fashionable to have ribbons etc. starched into a series of tight, narrow pleats, passable results could be obtained by laying the damp ribbon on a wooden crimping board (658), running a grooved roller over it, and setting it aside to dry. To achieve a superior finish, and virtually instant results, it was necessary to invest in one of the much more expensive crimping machines (659-663), which had polished brass rollers heated by short iron slugs (663).

Just outside the back 'ouze door, a wood-framed meat safe with sides of perforated zinc hung from the wall, close to the wood-cased pump with its large granite trough, the **pump-traw**. From here, a range of outbuildings extended along the eastern side of the back court or backlet. First came the **wood-** and **turf-'ouze** for the storage of firewood and turf.

Peat-cutting on Dartmoor was a midsummer activity, Mr Pearse of Walkhampton near Princetown describing to Mrs Fielden how various tools were used to work the deeper **turf-ties**. Firstly the slitting knife (1470) marked out and cut the sides of the surface vegetation, known either as the *spending*, *spine*, or *sward*, which was then stripped off with a half-round bladed *butting-*, *spurting-*, or *spending-ire* (1471). This revealed the true peat, which was dug out by thrusting the L-sectioned blade of a **turf-ire** (1469) vertically into it, and raising a long rectangular block on to the surface, where it was left to dry out over the following months. In the lower moorland, particularly around Chagford and Widecombe, only the peaty surface of the moors was used, the thick turves called fags or vags (the equivalent of the North-country *fleights*) being marked out, cut vertically, sliced horizontally, and lifted out using just a single tool, a broad, slightly curved **vag-ire** (1468). When peat cutting had been completed, these various tools were carefully cleaned, and then had their blades wound with straw rope, which kept them dry and reduced the risk of accidents from their sharp edges. By the early autumn both peats and vags had dried out completely, and were carried back in **slides** or **sleds** to the farm for use throughout the coming year.

Beyond the turf-'ouze lay the cellar, a room at ground level, fitted with long, low wooden benches or stillages called **jibs**, where the household's supplies of home-brewed beer and cider were stored in casks. Here the spile pins, spigots (995-996), cork bungs and the mallets for tapping them into the barrels were all to hand, along with the funnels or **tunners** used when filling them with liquor. In later times, the iron drum which held paraffin oil for the lamps was kept here too, the cellar's cool temperature and locked door rendering it both safe and secure.

The north side of the backlet, parallel to the farmhouse, was occupied by the **pound-'ouze** which housed the cider press, and the **brew-'ouze** with its furnace, tubs and coolers, where all the farm's everyday drinks were manufactured.

Between them a gate led through to the kitchen garden, a plot enclosed by thatch-

topped cob walls, against which fruit trees were trained. This area was chiefly used by the farmer to grow vegetables for his own household, but one corner was his wife's herb garden, stocked with sage, mint, thyme, rue, marjoram, balm, rosemary, lavendar, 'boy's love' and bergamot for both culinary and medicinal use, as well as pennyroyal for making **organ-tay**. Nearby her bee-skeps, or **bee-butts**, stood on stone plinths sheltered within bee-boles hollowed out of the cob walls, ready to provide her stores of honey.

Returning across the backlet, a narrow, tiled lean-to roof supported on four oak posts could be seen to protect the north side of the farmhouse. Known as the **skilling**, it ensured that the outer walls and windows of the dairy and cheese room remained in cool shadow throughout the heat of the day, and also provided a well-ventilated shady covered area where the dairy utensils could dry and sweeten after scalding, without risk of shrinkage and drying out.

On entering the drang-way at its northern end, a doorway on the eastern side lead into the dairy, a room sunk two feet below ground level so as to keep it particularly cool. In order to exclude cats, birds and dust, but still provide a good circulation of fresh air, the window was covered with a thick perforated iron sheet, this later being replaced by the factory-made perforated zinc. A bench, usually slate-topped, but occasionally of wood at the older farms, ran around three sides of the dairy to support a row of broad, deep brass cream-pans (1420-21) these later being replaced by glazed earthenware examples.

Mrs Hook of Chumleigh explained the traditional manner of making cream to Mrs Fielden in the 1930s: milk from the five o'clock afternoon milking was strained through a clean muslin into the cream pans and left overnight to allow the cream to rise to the surface. Each pan was then put over hot cinders, perhaps on one of the chafing dishes (1424-5) or stoves (1423) made for this purpose, and heated until 'a head comes on top of the milk [with] a ring rising in the centre'. At this point the cream-pan was replaced in the dairy for its second night, so that the thick, semi-solid **scald**, **clotted** or **clouted cream** set on top of the milk, from which it could then be lifted off next morning using a long-handled perforated brass skimmer (957-964).

In most parts of Britain, butter was made from raw cream, skimmed from the unheated milk twelve hours or more after milking, and then agitated in cylindrical or barrel-shaped churns. In Devon, however, churn butter was universally despised, for here it was hand-turned from clotted cream.[9] First a shallow wooden butter tub (1428-32) was scalded with boiling water, and then rinsed with fresh, cold pump-water, to ensure that the cream would not stick to the wood. The cream was then poured in, and the farmer's wife used her hand, similarly washed in really hot water and then in cold, to agitate the cream, working it with a steady, gentle circular motion, always in the same direction, keeping the hand flat, until the butter came. This might take anything from half to three hours or more, depending on the weather. Having squeezed the butter into a lump, the buttermilk was then poured off and the butter washed in three or four waters before the salt could be worked in and the butter finally worked up with scotch hands (1438-41) or prints (1443-48) into a roll or a block ready for sale. These operations could all be carried out on the slate-topped table in the middle of the dairy, but frequently butter-making was done in the back-'ouze sink, where cold water was readily available.

Through the door in the east wall of the dairy lay the cheese room. The actual cheesemaking process started in the back kitchen fireplace where the whole milk, or

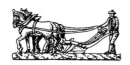

the scald milk from beneath the clotted cream, was gently warmed in the great brass dish-kettle (1449). The rennet, made from cured calves' stomachs, was then added to transform it into a mass of soft curds. These were then drained in a wooden drainer (1453), packed into muslin-lined cooper-made cheese vats (1451), covered with a sinker (1452), and placed in the cheese press which squeezed out the whey and compressed the curds into a hard, solid cheese.

Perhaps the earliest type of cheese press used in Devon employed a long weighted lever to exert an even but variable pressure. Most of the later presses used heavy stones as weights, raising and lowering them with iron screws or with windlasses as required,[10] although screw presses (1454) and improved lever mechanisms continued to be used in the county (1455).

On being removed from the press, the cheeses were left to ripen on the wooden racks which lined the cheese-room walls, being turned regularly until they matured and were ready for either sale or use.

On returning to the drang-way, turning left towards the vore-door, and left again into the next doorway, the parlour was entered. This room was used only on Sundays and on special occasions up to the later nineteenth century, when the farmer's daughters learnt to play and sing at the piano, and paying guests were given its use during their summertime holidays. Perhaps for them, the old stone floor had been taken up and replaced with one of timber planks, the new **boarden** or **planch** floors, when carpeted, being much warmer and drier, as long as they were free from dry rot. With this exception, however, the parlour retained most of its late Georgian furniture and fittings, the ceiling still being plastered between its main beams, as in the front kitchen.

Turning left from the doorway, and proceeding clockwise around the parlour, the first piece of furniture was the corner cupboard (333), its glazed upper section displaying chiney figures (461-517), the old hour-glass used principally to time both roasting and baking, **gramfer's** silver-cased 'turnip' watch with its verge movement, his **hornen** snuffbox (1193), and **sperticles** (spectacles), and the old punch ladle with its silver bowl and whalebone handle (cf.1159-1164), along with similar family treasures. Close by, midway along the north wall, stood an early nineteenth century piano, its tall mahogany case being French polished, and the space between its Corinthian pillars filled by a panel of pleated red silk. In other farms, the piano might be of the flat-topped 'square' design, but both varieties were unlikely to have been bought new, coming with the Canterbury and the music stool (307) from secondhand sales in the 1880s, when the farmer's daughters first began to learn music.

A boxed-in wooden staircase leading up to the chambers occupied the next corner, this being followed by the the chimney stack, originally intended for a large hearth fire, but then partly built up to receive an elegant cast-iron hob-grate of about 1800. Its neat surround was topped by a mantle-piece on which stood a 'parlour looking-glass' or chimney-glass in a French-polished rosewood frame with gilt-wood caps and bases to its columns. Before it, in the centre of the mantlepiece, there was a parlour clock (380), perhaps one of the 'skeleton' type with its exposed brass movement protected by a glass dome. Lustre candlesticks, with dangling cut glass pendants to catch the light, stood at each end, the remaining space being filled with small Staffordshire pottery animals (558-566 & 576-578), cottages (500-505), and a dome-covered vase of wax flowers.

Around the fireplace itself there was a copper kettle (1037) on the hob, a brass trivet (810, 812) on the top firebar, a large fender with burnished steel fire irons (114-

Farmers' jugs and mugs from the Leeds, Staffordshire and Sunderland potteries were usually displayed on the chiffonier in the parlour (top row: 1134, 1135, 1187, bottom row: 1132, 1183, 1184, 1131).

115 & 117-120), and an upholstered fender-stool standing on the hearth rug. This was one of the traditional **clip-rugs** or **rag-mats** made by the labourers' wives and daughters, who sewed clippings of coloured cloth on to lengths of strong canvas to produce very comfortable and durable rugs.

Sitting before the fire, either on the leather-covered 'grandfather chair', or the Windsor rocking chair (319), both with their box footstools with padded wool-work tops (308) must have been very pleasant on a winter's evening. The round rosewood table close at hand had at its centre a stuffed owl under a glass dome, this and the large family bible both standing on coloured wooden mats, alongside one or more photo albums and framed photographs and daguerreotypes of relations past and present. Each Sunday morning in summer a bowl of roses or other flowers was displayed here, these becoming ever more **davered** or faded until replaced a week later.

Leaving the fireplace area, and passing the door which led into the dining room, the furniture along the south wall of the parlour commenced with a mahogany

chiffonier. Its base had a large double-doored cupboard topped by a long narrow drawer and a flat top, above which rose an arch-topped mirror flanked by two small shelves. This was one of the main display stands, its top being crammed with all manner of nick-nackery. The centre was filled by a large glass dome of coloured wax flowers, with a lustre candlestick to each side, these being surrounded by early Toby jugs, cow creamers, with the mouth forming the spout and the tail the handle (568-574), and both farming jugs (1131-1136) and farming mugs (1183-1187) with their well-known verses.

The three-light lattice window nearby faced south to attract the maximum sunshine and give pleasant views of the colourful flowerbeds of the front garden, its window ledge providing further space for more flowering plants and ferns. Here, ideally placed in full daylight, stood a small round walnut table, its top lifting up to reveal a workbox lined in red silk holding everything required for needlework. Beyond this, backing against the drang-way wall, stood a long six-seater mahogany couch, its curved

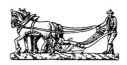

The model ships, ships in bottles, nautical prints and sailor's glass rolling pins displayed in the Devon farm-house parlour all reflect Devon's rich nautical heritage. Few of these record dramatic adventures at sea nearly so vividly as this remarkable painting which shows the rescue of the wrecked Buckland, *owned and commanded by William Bartlett of St Marychurch, as she returned from Newfoundland to Torbay in the winter of 1755 (583).*

ends, arched back, bolsters and cushions all being upholstered in black horsehair. At Chrismastime this made a convenient spare bed.

Other furnishings included five or six 'country Chippendale' chairs with ladder-, spindle-, or splat -backs, an early oak bible box (337-339) or desk (342), unless these had been committed to the lumber room, and perhaps a spinning wheel or bobbin-winder. Mr Chope could not remember seeing these in use, since home spinning had ceased in the early nineteenth century, but he did hear people speak of it, and an old lady was once pointed out to him as the last spinster.[11]

Finally, the decoration of this already crowded room was completed by covering virtually every available area of wall-space with numerous ornaments. There were framed pictures of farming, agricultural, biblical and naval subjects, paintings on glass, cut paperwork (587-592), pin-prick pictures (592), samplers (594-620), and pink-lustred Sunderland wall-plaques inscribed 'PREPARE TO MEET THY GOD'(582). There were glass walking sticks (424), bells, witch-balls (417-421), and hollow blown-glass rolling pins. Even in the 1920s most Devon farmhouses and

cottages still had one of these. Known as 'Bristol Rollers' they were probably made in that city, or at nearby Nailsea, and carried into Devon by the coastal trade. After making enquiries, Charles Laycock was able to record that they had been used in various

Charles Laycock's parlour at Moretonhampstead, with its clip rug, local Windsor chair, numerous pictures, and early eighteenth century long-case clock by W. Clemence of Totnes. The spinning wheel is Swiss, an example of the mass of continental folk art brought into this country from the 1890s to satisfy the demands of English collectors.

ways, either as containers for gin or eau-de-Cologne, imported or smuggled by sailors as gifts for sweethearts, or as practical rolling pins, for which they were ideally cool and heavy when filled with either cold water or sand. As love-tokens they could be hung up on ribbons in the parlour. So long as they remained there, the sailor lover was safe, but, should they fall down and break, this was a sure sign that he had been ship-wrecked and would probably never return.

This nautical theme was continued with model ships in cases (453-455), ships in bottles (444-452), and shell ornaments (456-458), the latter being made as tourist souvenirs in the popular south Devon seaside resorts.

Passing through into the dining room, there was a complete change of character and period. In contrast to the fussy details, imported timbers and well-upholstered furnishings of the late Georgian and early Victorian parlour, the dining room represented the solid, somewhat austere values of Stuart England. At this time the yeoman farmer was of comparatively high status, quite the social equal of the doctor, attorney, merchant or even the parson. He had enjoyed a good social and sporting life, with his dining room frequently used to entertain numerous guests, but by the mid nineteenth century his finances, his education and his dialect all left him completely outranked by his former colleagues. Now the dining room was hardly ever used, only being opened up for the rare visits of his landlord, his prospective MP, or his squire's shooting party. As a result, the whole room remained virtually unchanged as a two-hundred year old time-capsule set within an otherwise developing household.

The plaster ceiling was finely moulded, and the floor made of broad oak boards waxed to a deep polish. Immediately to the left of the door, the wide hearth-place was furnished with an iron dog-grate, a fine cast-iron fireback (86-87), and a granite coping instead of a fender. On the carved oak mantlepiece, beneath the plaster coat of arms bearing a seventeenth century date on the chimney breast, stood a bracket clock (381) which struck the hours and quarters on eight bells. Massive bronze vases and fine old silver candlesticks stood to each side. Opposite the fireplace, along the centre of the room, stood a polished oak dining table, its bulbous turned legs joined by stretchers close to ground level. Oak armchairs stood at each end, with four staight-backed dining chairs aligned down each side.

A large oak press-cupboard occupied the centre of the north wall. It had a single cupboard below, and two smaller ones above, each recessed beneath a flat top supported by a turned column at each end. The top was used for the display of some fine old silver, tankards, flagons, and a pair of salvers, along with a central copper tea-urn, various cut-glass decanters and rummers, and an inlaid wooden tea-caddy (357-363), knife box and bread-truckle. Turning to the east wall, a long oak settle stood next to an eight-day grandfather clock and an oak corner-cupboard containing a collection of old willow-pattern china, while a small gate-legged table stood nearby, beneath the latticed window. This, together with old family portraits and various hunting and cockfighting scenes, completed both the furnishings of the dining room, and our tour of the ground floor.

As far as the six bedrooms were concerned, they were served by the staircases in the front and back kitchens and that in the parlour. This meant that some of the bedrooms could only be entered by passing through one, or even two, of the others. They were all floored with broad elm planks, had ceilings a little over six feet high, wiith sloping sections following the line of the steep thatched roofs down to the

level of the eaves, and were lit by latticed casement windows, each beneath its individual dormer gable. There were no fireplaces, but numerous built-in cupboards, fitted either with shelves or iron hooks, served the function of wardrobes and chests of drawers.

The farmer's own bedroom, above the south-facing front kitchen, had a large oak four-poster bed. Charles Laycock remembering his grandfather (the paternal one in Huddersfield, or a maternal one in Devon?) sleeping in one of these, with all the curtains pulled close, his night-cap on, and the windows tightly shut, even on a hot summer's night! Here too stood an oak **pair 'o drawers** (chest of drawers) of the tallboy type, a couple of Windsor chairs, and perhaps an old oak cradle (368). In the room over the back kitchen, the children and farm servants slept in iron-framed beds with slightly-arched heads, the remaining rooms having half-tester beds with a canopy and curtains only at the upper end.

The small room over the porch might serve as an additional bedroom, but here it was used as a lumber-room, further storage for keeping apples, seed potatoes, onions etc. being available in the cock-loft which occupied the space between the bedroom ceilings and the ridge of the thatched roof.

Having completed the tour of the farmhouse, we can now go out into the farmyard, and look at the implements which were used for various purposes throughout the farming year, starting with the preparation of the land.

Clearing rough land, removing its coarse vegetation, gorse and brushwood, and making it ready to receive crops, was one of the hardest tasks ever to be performed on the farm. Much of this work was carried out using hand tools, such as the **beating-axe**, **bait-ex**, or **biddix**, a heavy adze with a blade five or six inches wide by a foot long, with a slightly scooped profile ideal for chopping the soil into large chunks. Where roots had to be grubbed out, a **two-bill**, **visgy**, or **bisgy** (1322) was used, this having a horizontal blade like a small beating axe on one side, and a vertical axe blade on the other.

Breast ploughs, known as **spades** (1327) in Devon, had their broad-pointed iron blade mounted on a long wooden shaft topped by a flat cross-piece or **drift** formed as a handle at both ends. Holding the drift with both hands, the labourer thrust his loins against it, driving the blade under the turf and shallow roots until he had undercut some twelve or fifteen inches. Then, by giving the drift a hefty twist, the turf was torn loose, this being made much easier if the blade had a vertical edge or coulter at one side, or if the cut had previously been nicked across at convenient lengths. If the land was suitable, the same effect could be obtained by fitting a flat **velling share** (1328) to a plough, then using horses to pull it through the soil.

Whichever method had been used to pare the land, the turf etc. was now left for a while to rot and to break up, after which it was pulled to pieces with rough harrows, bruised with a granite or moorstone roller, and worked with light harrows to shake the earth out of the dry vegetation or **beat**. This was then drawn together with a **drudge** or **clum**, a six-inch square beam, six feet long, with perhaps seventeen two-inch wide wooden teeth, eighteen inches long, portruding from its bottom surface. Four handles at the back enabled two men to control it as a horse dragged it across the field, gathering the beat first into rows, and then into heaps.

Long-toothed hand rakes were more effective in separating the dried vegetation from the earth, but they required much more time and labour. The heaps of beat were now shaken up light and hollow, primed with a handful of rough straw, set alight, and tended until they had burnt out

completely, after which their ashes were spread across the field.

To prepare the seedbed, the soil was turned over and broken up using a plough or, to use the Devon word, a **zole**, coming from the Old English for a plough, *solh*. From the medieval period these had been made entirely of wood, except for the coulter which made the vertical cut, and the share, which cut horizontally, and these were both of iron.

The Derby plough (1329), dating from the mid nineteenth century, represented the next stage of development, being constructed entirely of iron, except for its beam and handles, and having an adjustable wheel to regulate the depth of the furrow. Where the fields were steeply sloping, there might be problems both in turning the plough at each end of the furrow, and in ensuring that the furrows were all turned up-hill to counteract the natural downward progression of the soil. For these reasons two-way zoles (1330) were developed, these having a coulter etc. at each end, and handles pivoting at the centre of the beam, so that they could work in either direction. The **grute-wrest** or mould-board was hinged, to throw the soil to left or right, as required, while the **head-taws** at each end were joined by an iron bar, so that the hook linking the plough to the horses or oxen could simply slide from one end to the other as they walked around before commencing the next furrow.

Four oxen formed the usual Devon **plough**, this word referring to the team itself, and not to the actual implement. Instead of having collars like horses, they wore yokes (1246), strong wooden beams specially shaped to fit over the shoulders of each pair, with a stout wooden bows passing around their necks to hold it in place, and a central iron link to attach it to the plough gear. Their role as draught animals was entirely taken over by horses during the nineteenth century, one of the last pairs of oxen to work in the county being recorded in East Devon in 1878.

After ploughing, the fields were harrowed, the museum's mid-Victorian example of a **drag** (1332-3) being made with two frames hinged together, each one having four cross-strips called **zoards** (swords) passing through four **larras** (beams). Chains linked the two adjustable iron head-taws to each end of the **whippentree** (whippletree) drawn behind the horses, so that as the harrow was dragged along at an angle, each of its forty spikes left behind its own parallel line in the soil, and left no part unstirred.

Some seeds may have been sown using **dibbling irons** (1334-5), but most Devon sources refer to corn of all kinds being sown broadcast from a deep kidney-shaped wooden (later galvanised sheet iron) tray called a **zellup** or seedlip (1336), seed being thrown out by the left hand as the right leg went forward, and vice versa.

As the sower walked the length of the field he sowed with his right hand, then transferring to the left as he returned back in the opposite direction. At Hartland they said:

'When the say-gulls cry by lan',
'Tis time to tak the zellup in han':
When the say-gulls cry by say,
'Tis time to draw the zellup away',

thus using the gulls as a weather forecast for forthcoming rain.

Sowing by hand, a skilled operation, was still being practiced to a very small extent in the 1930s, but for forty years some farmers had adopted a mechanical broadcasting device called a fiddle (1337). This light wood-framed hopper was slung from a web over the sower's shoulder, a rotating wheel scattered the seed out in a wide, relatively even spread as he used one hand drawn a fiddle-like bow to and fro.

Once the field had been sown, it was lightly harrowed and then rolled to cover

over the seeds. At this stage flocks of birds could swoop down to eat large quantities of the seed, and so boys armed with rattles and clappers (1338-9) were employed to keep them away. As the season progressed weeds became a major problem, and had to be removed by women who used **spitters** or **spuds**, square-bladed tools on long handles, the ordinary Kentish or Canterbury hoes being reserved mainly for thinning and weeding turnips.

At harvest time, wheat was cut with a **reaping hook** (1340) similar in shape to a sickle, but with a broader, smooth-edged blade. Similar tools called **browse-** or **brawl-hooks** (1317-18) had much heavier blades, being used for trimming the tall Devon hedges, or for cutting brushwood. In the harvest field, each man used his reaping hook, grasped in his right hand, to cut into the base of the straw, just above the ground, simultaneously striking it halfway up with his left hand and arm. Having gathered together as much as would form a sheaf, he supported it between his left arm and leg before making a second cut which freed it completely from the ground. The hook then came into use again, raising the bottom end of the sheaf up into a horizontal position, so that it could be bound with a band of combed wheat straw. Women worked with a smaller **hand greeping hook**, gripping the wheat with the left hand and cutting it with the right, six of these small **greeps** making up a single sheaf. For mowing, the **zie** (scythe) (1341) was used, its **snead** (shaft) having two **hand-pins** (handles) and a ring and wedges to secure the blade, all these being adjustable to suit the proportions of the user.

The loose corn left after reaping was sometimes collected by women using ordinary wooden hand-rakes, but mowers were always followed by **tathers**, women or boys who gathered up the corn into bundles using **tathing hooks** (1343-47) of round iron bar, or **tathing-** or **scoring-rakes** about

a foot wide with four or six long teeth. Men called **benders** (binders) then formed the bundles into sheaves, bound them with wheat straw bands, and set them up as stitches or stooks.

Afterwards the field was raked over again with an **errish rake** (1348-49), *erse* being the Old English word for a stubble field. This very large rake was pulled along, the right hand gripping the cross-piece between the two branches, while the left passed in front of the chest to hold the handle, enabling the rake to be steadied or lifted as work progressed. For gathering hay, a horse-drawn **tumble-jack** or American hay-rake was regularly used from the mid nineteenth century, this replacing much of the earlier labour-intensive hand-held hay rakes. Once the sheaves of corn had thoroughly dried out in the stook, they were transported back to the farm either in carts or on pack-horses.

As Celia Fiennes travelled from Ashburton to Plymouth in 1698, she had noted how the lanes were:

'exceeding narrow and so cover'd up, you can see little about [you]... the wayes now became so difficult that one could scarcely pass by each other, even single horses, and so dirty in many places and just a track for one horse's feet'[13]

A century later, William Marshall stated that a pair of wheels was not seen on a West Country farm before the 1770s, ox sleds being used for the harvest, and small one-horse or ox-sled carts for carting manure. From that time, however, wheeled transport gradually began to increase, although the large waggons drawn by teams of horses, each with belfries (1269-70) mounted on their hames to forewarn on-coming traffic, never became common here, as they did in those counties lying further to the east. This late introduction of wheeled transport meant that pack-horses continued to be used in Devon perhaps up to the mid nine-

Pack-horses were a major form of transport in Devon, as recorded in W.H. Pyne's drawing of a 'Devonshire Carrier' published in 1808 (top left). The other drawings show the horses carrying the sheaves of corn to the farm on long crooks (top right), galloping back to the harvest field (bottom left), and with manure piled high above their dung pots (bottom right).

teenth century, or even later, for in the 1890s Dr Karkeek was still able to collect a full set of pack-saddles from Exmoor, together with all their accessories.

The saddles themselves (1259-60) are made of two deep wooden end-bows, each made from two planks, cross halved together, nailed, and braced with iron bands. The bows are joined by a series of planks shaped to follow the contours of the horse's back, a gap being left down the centre to prevent any direct pressure on the spine. Beneath the planks, a shaped pad made of combed wheat straw sewn into a canvas cover is secured by thongs, this providing a firm 'breathing' absorbent layer between the hard wood and the horse. Once in place, the pack saddle was secured by a **hairen gease** or **sissing girt**, a special girth made partly of horsehair webbing and partly of rope, which passed over the saddle and completely around the belly. Two or three

narrow bags of lime could now be thrown across the saddle, but for other loads further equipment was required. For dung, sand, roadbuilding materials etc., pairs of pots (1261-64) linked together by hooked chains were slung over the saddle, lighter loads such as dung then being piled up over the saddle before the journey commenced. On arrival, a peg could be withdrawn from a hole in the outer upright, allowing the whole base to swing open and dump the load wherever it was needed. Cordwood, large stones and other heavy items were carried on **crubs** or **short-crooks** (1267-68) made either from naturally bent timbers, or from frames fastened at right-angles by strong iron hinges. In either case, their upper ends were fastened by pegs which passed through holes drilled in the two end bows of the saddle. Much larger **crooks** (1265-66) made of bent willow poles some seven or eight feet long, were used when

carrying sheaves of corn. Once the crooks had been mounted across the saddle, the sheaves were packed in by hand, each having its top placed next to the bottom of its neighbour, all having their butts facing outwards. When the upper part of the load had been piled high above the horse's back with a **peck** or fork, the peck was set under one of the cross-bars of the crooks, one end of the **balsh** or **balsh-rope** tied to it, the other end being thrown over the load, pulled down and tied to hold the whole stack firmly in place. A boy then led a string of laden horses along the lanes and tracks at a steady pace, until they reached the rick-yard or barn. Here the rope was removed, and the fork used to push the upper part of the load back over the horse's tail, either on to the ground, or on to a cloth placed there to receive it.

When the lower part of the load had been removed by hand, and the whole string of horses unloaded, the boy mounted the saddle, standing upright on the crooks, and trotted, or even galloped his horses back to the field. This must have made an alarming prospect for any on-coming traffic, but, as a local saying records:

'*He hath'n a-got no more manners*
Than a 'oss an' a pair o' pang'ers!'

To keep the corn free from the depredations of rats and mice, it was stacked up on a **mowstead**, a loose wooden framework supported on two-foot high **mow-stones** or **staddle-stones** surrounded by circular projecting **helens** of slate. Instead of lifting up the corn with a long-handled pitch-fork with U-shaped tines, as in many other parts of the country, the Devon farmer used a peck (1351-52) with a short handle and a pair of closely-set curving tines.[14]

First a boy would place a sheaf in front of the pitcher, a man who speared it with his peck, and then flung it high over his head using the combined spring of his arms and legs, or working at arm's length. If the height was very great, or the sheaf very heavy, one man would place the tines of his peck beneath the stem or handle of the pitcher's, so that they could send it soaring upwards to the top of the stack, where it was caught by a man with another peck, and tossed into place.

Both **mows** of corn and **ricks** of hay were thatched with **longstraw**, which was made by taking a handful of thrashed straw in both hands, separating the hands to divide it in the middle, and then shaking out the short straws. Bundles formed in this way were then laid on top of the stack to form a waterproof roof. They were firmly held in place with straw ropes made from reed (combed wheat straw). Mr Chope described how this was made using a **wink**, **spinner**, or **skeiner** mounted on a crowbar driven into a wall. It had a 'rotary skeleton drum having spider arms, of which those in front were notched at the ends. The rope, as it is made from the dampened reed, is wound upon the body of the drum, and is passed through one of the notches, so that, as the ropemaker moves his hand and inserts fresh reed into it, he causes the wink to rotate and spin a fresh length of rope. When the wink is full, the rope is unwound from it and rewound into a large ball called a clew about 2 feet 6 inches in diameter'.

Mrs Fielden collected a wink which had its long handle thrust into the side of a rick, its square frame being rotated by a jerk of the spinner's hand as he walked backwards, pulling out the rope (1479).

In use, the straw rope was first laid horizontally across the long-straw thatch, being carried from one end to the other with a **roping-pole**. These **long-ropes** were then pegged down along their length with **spears** (sticks split from willow or hazel, pointed at both ends and doubled like a staple) driven into the thatch. The more secure **nibs** (hooked sticks) held down both ends. **Thort-ropes** (short ropes) were then twisted round the long-ropes, large pebbles called

mow-stones being tied to their bottom ends, these resting on the edge of the thatch, preventing it from being blown away.

Later, in the autumn, some of the sheaves would be thrown down from the mow, taken to the barn, and heaped in a **zess** or pile at one or both sides of the wooden floor which extended between the wide front and back doors. It was then set out in two rows, with the ears together in the middle, and beaten with a **threshel**, **drashel**, or flail (1356-63). This tool had two sections, a hand-stave or handle of hazel or ash, and a **vlail** (flail) of **holm** (holly). On some flails one end of the hand-stave was sheathed in leather or rawhide to form the **toad's head**, while the end of the vlail was similarly sheathed to form the **keeple**, **keeble**, or **capel**, both being sewn with thongs said to be made feom eelskin.

Other flails had **kibbles** formed from a bent piece of wood or cow-horn, but in either case, the two separate sections were linked by a loop of leather or rawhide called a **middle been**, its ends joined together with a wooden peg. This gave a very flexible but also very strong joint. Such tools were still being used, and also made, on Dartmoor farms in the 1930s. Since the farmers here only grew enough corn for their own use, they found flails to be far more economical and convenient than the hire of a threshing machine, and they could also be used for beating the dust out of fleeces.

Mrs Fielden noted how a skillful thresher changed over the beat of his flail from left to right without changing rythm, two men standing opposite each other whirling their flails around their heads before each blow fell alternately down flat across the ears of corn keeping perfect harmony. It was said that 'Two vlails an' a gookoo' was the labourer's version of a musical concert.

If barley was being threshed, its long, tough **awns** could resist the action of the flail, and so they had to be removed by stamping the grain beneath the parallel iron bars of a **piler** (1364-68) as it was rapidly beaten up and down on the boards of the threshing floor.

To separate the grain from the chaff and broken straw, it had traditionally been carried out on horseback to a nearby windy summit, where women **'heaved'** it from a **zemmet** or blind sieve (1369) down on to a canvas **win-sheet** laid on the ground, the wind carrrying off the light chaff etc., leaving only the cleaned, heavy grain on the canvas.

The same operation was carried out between the barn doors, a **machine-fan** or **winding-van** (1371) creating an artificial draught for this purpose. This device was still being used at Lower Rocombe and Cockington near Torquay in the 1930s, but from about 1870 winnowing machines (1372) had come into general use. In the larger farms these were set up in the barn, being powered either by an engine or by an iron shaft which passed through the wall to a horse-wheel in the roundhouse.

The machines carried out the winnowing process much more effectively and could **case** the corn, separating the larger grains from the smaller, thus replacing the laborious use of hand-sieves with different meshes, variously called **whait-**, **barley-** or **wut-** (oat) **casers**. The final cleaning of the grain remained a hand process for some time however, small sieves with very fine meshes being **rewed** around with a circular motion which left the good corn at the circumference, the loose corn and husks in the middle, and the small weed seeds and dust on the ground.

If required for food, the corn was then carried off to the miller, who ground it between the stones (1380--82) and returned it as flour, meal and bran after deducting a certain quantity as his toll.

Barley was sometimes sent off for malting too, although some of the farms even had

their own malthouses to produce the main raw ingredient for their home-brewed ales.

For other crops, cultivation was a much simpler matter, potatoes, for example, only requiring to be earthed up with a ridging plough (1331) and dug up with a two-pronged **digging-maddick** or **digger** (1323-4 and 1350).

Any wheat straw which was required for thatching buildings was not stacked in mows, but was piled up loosely in the barn. The grain had to be threshed out very carefully, for it was essential that the straw, known as **reed**, remained as straight and unbruised as possible. The older method had been to cut off the ears and thresh them separately, but bundles of the straw could also be gripped with both hands and then beaten either on the barn floor, over a cask, or whipped on a **whipping-horse** (1473) which effectively removed the grain, but left the empty ears still in place.

To remove the short straws and ensure that the reed lay parallel, a large double handful was held up to a short rope fixed high above the labourer's head, the rope then being wound round this small sheaf just below the ears, a small iron hook at the rope's end being looped around the vertical part of the rope, thus forming a noose, which was pulled tight. While held in this position, all the short straws and weeds were removed with a **reed-comb** (1474-78), after which the rope was unhooked, and the clean, straight, unbruised reed returned to the floor, perhaps being threshed once more to remove any remaining grain.

From the late nineteenth century this operation was usually carried out by using a reed-combing machine in which a rapidly-revolving spiked drum fitted either on top of a threshing machine which travelled from one farm to another, or in the barn, where it was powered by either an engine or the horse wheel. After being combed, the reed was made up into sheaves called **wads** or **nicky-wads** ready for thatching, six wads

being made up into a **knitch** or **nitch** if they were to be sold at this stage.

When starting to thatch a roof, the thatcher first sprinkled the reed with water to make it easier to pack down tightly. Propping his ladder against the wall near the right-hand corner of the roof, he began to tie the first row of wads to the rafters, using tar-cord and a thatcher's needle. Long iron skewers with hooked tops, known as **wall-crooks** were driven down into the top of the cob wall to hold the thatch in place here, preventing the wind from lifting the thatch from beneath its over-hanging eaves. Successive wads were then carried up to the thatcher, or passed to him on a **prang** (fork) by his **tender**, or assistant, each being tied in place, row upon row, until he could no longer work from his ladder. A wooden frame with two or three long iron tines, called a **datcher's ladder**, **standing bittle**, or **bittle-frame** (1482) was then stuck into the new thatch to provide firm rungs to support his weight. Knee caps, or **strads** (1487-88), the leathers which covered the front of his shins and knees, were particularly important now, as he worked directly on the surface of the thatch. After one side of the roof had been completed, he pared it down from ridge to eaves with a **datcher's hook** (1485) and pressed and smoothed it with a **smoothing-board** (1483-84) to achieve a perfectly even, neat slope, the cut end of each straw acting as a miniature water-spout to throw off the rain.

To finish the ridge, wads were bent over the top and secured by having rods, usually arranged in a diagonal pattern, pegged down into the thatch with spears split, trimmed to length and sharpened with a spar-hook.

Thus completed, the thatched roof could effectively keep the house waterproof and well-insulated for twenty or thirty years. It could then have an additional layer of thatch speared down on top of it to prolong its life still further, this process often being

repeated two or even three times before the whole thatch had to be removed down to the rafters and the whole process started again.

When Charles Laycock started to renovate his house in Moretonhampstead around 1909, he found that the thatch had been re-covered so many times that it was over six feet thick, suggesting that new top layers had been repeatedly added since the roof was last thatched around 1700.

The use of straw grown on the farm for thatching the farmhouse, successfully completes this tour of the traditional Devon barton. It has been a remarkably rich and well-informed tour, led by the most observant and interesting of guides, who have described where and how all those artefacts now in the museum were used by the people of rural Devon in the middle of the nineteenth century.

Everyone interested in traditional ways of life, either in Devon, in these islands, or in Europe and beyond, owes a great debt of gratitude to the foresight of Charles Laycock, Mrs M.E. Fielden and R.P. Chope, for, without their efforts, virtually none of these artefacts and their related information would have been preserved for the benefit of all future generations.

Notes

1. P.Q. Karkeek 'White Ale', *Trans. Devon. Assoc.* (1877)

2. R.P. Chope, 'Some old Farm Implements and Operations' *Trans. Devon. Assoc.* L (1918) 269-292

3. Rev.S.Rowe. *Perambulations of the Ancient and Royal Forest of Dartmoor* (Plymouth 1848) 275

4. P.Brears *Traditional Food in Yorkshire* (Edinburgh 1987) 54

5. 'X.Y.Z.' 'Old Methods of Obtaining Fire and Light' & C.H.Laycock 'Obtaining Fire and Light' *Devon & Cornwall Notes & Querie*s (Exeter 1922-3) 165 & 84

6. P .Sambrook and P.Brears *The Country House Kitchen* (Stroud 1996)109

7. F. White *Good Things in England* (1932, 1974 ed.) 216. Martin Watts has also provided a classic recipe for a Shooting pudding of the kind usually boiled in a cloth, but in later years baked in a tin in the oven. It was cooked for his grandfather, W.J.V. Watts of The Firs, Newton Abbot, who carried a slab of it in his pocket, along with a flask of port mixed with brandy, to keep him going through a winter's day outdoors with his gun.

SHOOTING PUDDING

4oz (100g) currants	*6oz (150g) suet*
5oz (125g) raisins	*12oz (350g) self raising flour*
2oz (5g) chopped candied peel	*pinch of mixed spice*
a little milk	

1. Mix all the dry ingredients, then beat the egg with a little milk and stir this into the mixture, adding sufficient milk so that it will just drop off the spoon. 2. Put the mixture into a square greased tin and bake at 180˚C (350˚F), gas mark 4 until it is cooked and firm to the touch. 3. Leave in the tin until cool, then turn out.

8. R.P.Chope, *Devon & Cornwall Notes & Queries* XI (Exeter 1920-21) 308 & 302

9. W.H. Pyne, *Costume of Great Britain* (London 1805) plXIII & J.Sarsby, 'Buttermaking the Devonshire Way' *Country Origins* (Nairn, Winter 1995) 19-23

10. R.P.Chope, 'Cheese Presses' *Devon & Cornwall Notes & Queries* 14 (Exeter 1927) 203.

11. R.P.Chope op cit. note 1, 269

12. Much of this section section is based on R.P. Chope's article above, which was written from the practical experience and memories obtained on his father's farm at Hartland in the latter half of the nineteenth century, together with reference to agricultural writers such as Marshall, Vancouver, etc.

13. C.Fiennes *The Journeys of Celia Fienne*s (1983ed.) 279

14. An identical fork is shown in the harvest scene in J. B. Bouttat's painting 'Kirkstall Abbey Delineated,1743' in Leeds City Museums.

An Introduction to the
Catalogue

The following catalogue describes every item given to the Torquay Museum to illustrate the traditional life on Devon farms of the mid nineteenth century. Social history material which does not directly relate to this theme, such as toys, musical instruments, costume, clay pipe bowls and a wealth of decorative art, including Charles Laycock's magnificent collection of 800 pieces of fine ceramics, have been omitted. The few pieces of related non-Devon social history, such as Friendly Society staff-heads, Biddenden Cake, Dorset owl, etc. have been included, however, for the benefit of people who otherwise would be unaware of their presence here.

The collections have been arranged according to the Social History and Industrial Classification (SHIC), which proceeds from community life, to domestic and family life, personal life, and working life. For convenience, individual groups and pieces have been brought together, professional baker's gingerbread moulds (working life) joining home baking equipment (domestic and family life), for example, so that all baking items can be seen together, and also to allow for the fact that we do not know if some items, such as oven forks, were used either by professional bakers, or in the home.

Each description starts with the catalogue number, followed by the name of the object, a brief physical description, and its dimensions in millimetres. These are followed by a series of museum numbers.

Originally each item was given both an individual number, which represented the order in which it had been received in a particular year, and another which gave the order in which it was received since the accessioning of the whole collection was started. Around 1990 a re-numbering programme was introduced, which gave each item a new running number, prefixed by a V. To illustrate this, the smoke jack, catalogue number 865, bears the numbers 340/1936 no.1852 V1449. This means that it was the 340th item received in 1936, the 1852nd item received since accessioning first began, and the 1449th item of social history re-numbered since c.1990. In addition, some items bear a number prefixed by an L, which relates to a list of items bequeathed by Charles Laycock in 1943. Regrettably the Fielden collection has no similar markings, since it came into the museum as a loan which was transformed into a single gift in 1935.

In practice, any actual specimen may have either all or none of the above numbers inscribed upon it. Therefore, to draw together every scrap of relevant information, all available sources have been thoroughly researched, these including the accessions registers, old labels, photographs of Charles Laycock's home, old museum displays etc. and illustrated articles in various journals etc.

The drawings have been designed to show the constructional features of each specimen. With few exceptions, they are either straight elevations or isometrics, every attempt being made to draw items on

each plate to a common scale. Where this has not proved possible, the plates have been divided by horizontal lines, to show where the scales have changed.

Collectors may be disappointed that no attempt has been made to give the date of each specimen. It has become customary for experts in the antiques trade to allocate precise dates to everything they deal with, but frequently these dates are based on little more than pure imagination. Fashionable objects, made for the use of polite society, can be closely dated solely on stylistic evidence, but this is not the case with traditional artefacts. In the 1930s Mrs Fielden found local smiths still producing brandises which had probably been made in precisely the same way from precisely the same materials, as they had been in the medieval period. Unless there is really sound evidence for dating such items, it is much better to leave them completely undated, rather than resort to entirely spurious inventions.

BIBLIOGRAPHY

P. Brears, *Horse Brasses.* (London 1981).

V. Chinnery, *Oak Furniture - The British Tradition.* (Woodbridge 1979).

R.P.Chope, *The Book of Hartland.* (p.238 lists his extensive bibliography).

R.P.Chope 'Some Old Farm Implements and Operations' *Trans.Devon.Assoc.* (Torquay 1918) pp268-292.

B.Cotton, *Windsor Chairs in the South West.* (Taunton c.1990).

W.Crossing, *Crossing's Dartmoor Worker.* (1903, republished Newton Abbot 1966 & 1992).

D.Eveleigh 'Cooking Pots & Old Curiosities; The Posnet and Skillet' *Folklife* 32 (Leeds 1994) pp7-32

M.E.Fielden 'Old Time Survivals in Devon' *Trans.Deon.Assoc* 66 (Plymouth 1934) 357-373

G.Friend, *Memories of Moretonhampstead.* (Tiverton 1989) p110 shows Charles Laycock, the tall man, sixth from the right.

C.H.Laycock: *Report & Transactions of the Devonshire Association:*
       41 (Plymouth 1909) pp89-92 'Supplementary Index to Verbal Provincialisms'
       41 pp298-300 'On the need for a Devonshire Dialect Grammar'
       46 (Plymouth 1914) pp359-371 'On Social Wasps in Devonshire'
       46 pp507-519 'On West Country Wit and Humour'
       49. (Plymouth 1917) pp296-319 'English National and Folk Music'
       52. (Plymouth 1920) pp158-191 ' The Old Devon Farm House I'
       53. (Plymouth 1921) 'Will-o'-the-Wisp'
       54 (Plymouth 1823) pp224-270 'The Old Devon Farm House II'
       55 (Plymouth 1924) pp154-181 do.,continued.
       72 (Torquay 1940) p59 'Devon Entomological Writings'
In addition, he edited the annual reports in the *Transactions* on 'Devonshire Verbal Provincialisms' from 1929, and on 'Devonshire Folk-Lore' from1938, up to the time of his death. His obituary was published in vol 75 (1943) p19.
The Devon Year Book
       (London 1915) pp121-136 'English Folk Music'
       (London 1921) p36 'Harvest Song'
       (London 1922) pp38-46 'The Old Devon Farm-house'
       (London 1924) pp62-68 'West-Country Dialect'
His obituary appeared in (London 1944) 22-23

Devon & Cornwall Notes & Queries:

12 (Exeter 1922-23) pp84-86 'Obtaining Fire & Light'

12 pp141-143 'Old Methods of Baking in the Devon Farmhouse'

12 p319 'West Country Dialect'

12 pp165-169 Correspondence on the above papers

14 (Exeter 1926-27) p200 'Teignhead'

15 (Exeter 1928-9) p10 & p199 'Jottings and Dottings'

15 p11 'Bushell' (dialect)

15 p110 'Hinkypunk'

15 p152 'Daphne or Dafny'(dialect).

P.Macdonald (ed), *Devon in Living Memory.* (Newbury & Exeter 1993).

C.N.Ponsford, *Devon Clocks & Clockmakers.* (Newton Abbot 1985).

Social History & Industrial Classification. (Sheffield 1983)

G.M.Spooner & F.S.Russell (eds.), *Worth's Dartmoor.* (1952, 2nd ed. Newton Abbot 1967)

R.Stanes, *The Old Farm.* (Exeter 1990).

The
Catalogue

Entry numbers in **bold** refer to illustrations that follow the listing, starting on page 107

CUSTOM & BELIEF

1. Communion flagon, pewter, unmarked except for the stamps 'BA' 'PC' on top of the handle. 268x120d 658/1899. Donated by H.L.Collins. From Nether Poppleford.

2. St Nectan biscuit. This was brought home to Mr R.P. Chope of Fosfelle, Hartland, Devon, by his housekeeper, who had received it at the service held in the parish church on 17 June 1936. c.55dx5 thick. V195 Fielden.

St Nectan, an early 6th century Celtic missionary, was beheaded at Hartland on 17 June by two robbers who had stolen his cows, but as proof of his sanctity he then picked up his head and carried it to the spring near his hut. When his grave was opened by the priest Brictric in the reign of Athelstan, a bone seal of his bust bearing the words 'SIGILLUM NECTANI' was discovered, this device being adopted on the medieval seals of Hartland Abbey, and later on these biscuits. The existing St Nectan's well at Hartland was given this name by Mr Chope, who may also have been responsible for introducing the biscuits too.

3. Biddenden Maids cake. One of a thousand rolls distributed to strangers on Easter Sunday afternoon, after service, along with five hundred loaves and cheese to the poor of Biddenden, Kent. This is traditionally believed to be in accordance with the will of Mary and Eliza Chulkhurst, Siamese twins who were born there in 1100, and died within six hours of each other thirty-four years later. 102x50x12 V121.

RITES OF PASSAGE

4. Pincushion,1806. Ribbed cream silk with pins stuck in to read 'A HAPPY TIME TO Mrs CRICHTON 1806' within a border of leaves on the front, and an oval panel to the rear. 160x105x59 V129.

5. Pincushion,1821. White satin woven with small sprigs of roses, with a pink,white and olive green at each corner, stuck with pins 'Welcome/Little/Stranger/1821/TB JB' with crowns, flowers, hearts and anchors. 151x111x69.

FRIENDLY SOCIETIES

6. Friendly Society staff head brass, on green painted wooden shaft, with a painted '74' 229x82 V519. This, together with nos.6 to 51, forms part of the collection donated by Major Gibbs, 346/1936, nos.1809-58 & 1864-7.

7. do. cast brass on turned wooden shaft with dark varnish. 1294x47 V521. no.1866.

8. do. as no.4. 1227x62 V522 no.1867.

9. do. cast brass 189x105 V474 no.1823 used at old Ottery and modern Ashcott.

10. do. 250x105 V1475 no.1836 as no.11 but without the acorn on top V1475 no.1836 'V' on barrel, used at Wanstrow.

11. do. 256x102 V476 no.1833 'J' on barrel, used at Walton near Street.

12. do. 248x98 V1477 no.1810 'K' on barrel, used at North Cadbury.

13. do. 242x106 V1478 no.1841 'F' on barrel, used at Paulton.

14. do. 231x85 V479 no.1829 'K' on barrel, used at South Petherton.

15. do. 187x55 V4780 no. 1848 engraved 'No.2', used at Shepton Beauchamp.

16. do. 158x50d V4781 no.1827 used at Pawlett.

17. do. 165x54d V4782 no.1839 used at Bower Hinton near Martock

18. do. 213x98 V483 no.1820 'U' on barrel, used at Woolavington

19. do. 250x111 V484 no.1832 'W' on barrel, used at Dowlish Wake

20. do. 217x85 V485 no.1845 used at Butleigh

21. do. 132x43 V486 no 1817 'G' on barrel, used at Nether Stowet

22. do. 208x63 V487 no.1838 'G' on barrel, used at Wembdon Hill

23. do. 117x40 V489 no.1815 used at Martock

24. do. 219x133 V488 no.1812 'B' on barrel, used at Chedzoy

25. do. 235x48 V490, no.1850, used at West Monkton
26. do. 208x55 V491 no.1844, milled band round knop, 'G' on barrel, used at Halberton

27. do. 208x179 V493 no.1818 'A' on barrel, used at Kilve

28. do. 223x104 V494 no.1816 'A' on barrel, used at Long Sutton

29. do. 300x116 V495 no.1809 'Z' on barrel, and stamped 'N'&'Y'

30. do. 303x147 V496 no. 1837 'C' on barrel, used at Marnhull, Dorset

31. do. 338x116 V497 no. 1831 stamped 'BLINMAN & CO / BRISTOL, 112', and with 'C' on barrel, used at Evercreech.

32. do. 274x116 V498 no.1828 'X' on barrel, used at Bruton

33. do. 317x142 V499 no.1840 'O' on barrel, used at Wincanton

34. do. 327x163 V500 no.1857, used at the Ship Inn, Stour near Gillingham, and at Fifehead, Dorset

35. do. 223x115 V501 no.1814 'H' on barrel, repaired with riveted plates, used at Ilchester and Tintinhull

36. do. 173x36d V502 no.1824, used at Kingstone near Taunton

37. do. 254x142 V503 no.1846. used at Stoke St Michael

38. do. 237x46 V504 no.1835 'F' on barrel, identical to no.20 used at West Monkton

39. do. 240x169 V505 no.1830 'D' on barrel, 'E' scratched on reverse, used at Pamborough

40. do. 206x152 V506 no.1826 'K' on barrel, used at Marston Biggot and Mells

41. do. 210x135 V507 no.1855, used by Bristol Shepherds

42. do. 189x108 V508 no.1849 milled bands and 'P' on barrel, used by Bristol Shepherds

43. do. 212x55 V509 no.1844 identical to no.26, used at Halberton

44. do. 152x93 V510 no.1822 'M' on barrel, used at Collumpton

45. do. 274x52 V511 no.1842 'G' on barrel, used at Bishops Lydeard

46. do. 149x61 V512 no.1825 'I' on barrel, used at Blagdon near Taunton

47. do. 133x72 V513 no.1819 milled bands and 'E' on barrel, used at Willerton

48. do. 172x72 V514 no.1821 milled bands and 'E' on barrel, used by Bristol Shepherds Society

49. do. 200x89 V515 no.1843 milled middle band and 'L' on barrel, used at Combe St Nicholas

50. do. 136x57 V516 no.1811 'W' on barrel, used at the Bell Inn, Stapleton, Glos.

51. do. 348x141 V517 no.1813 'Z' on barrel, used at Sutton Veney Justice

52. Key, iron, 122x44 V1094 no.746 For the chest in the Justices' room in the court at Kingsbridge, Devon, Donated by Mr Pickeard

POOR LAW RELIEF

53. Beggar's badge, 1827, pewter, 60d.x4 Sir Walter Scott described 'a long blue gown, with a pewter badge on the arm.all these marked at once a beggar by profession'. The 2nd Statistical Account states that in 1839 the Kirk Sessions on the Isle of Bute issued 24 badges authorising their holders to call for alms on Saturdays at the houses of the inhabitants of the parish, and it was understood that they obtained about two shillings each in this way, this method achieving 'a great effect in preventing general begging'.

POLICE

54. Constable's staff, 1793, walnut, the square head painted with (1) the Royal arms, (2) a shield painted argent, three lozenges gules, crest, a demi dog gules, (Pitcairn), (3) the monogram RF 1793 and (4) a red ensign flying in front of a blue ensign, with a ship's boat rowed by six men above, and a man-o'war below. 613x43x43 V3249 donated by Mr Hansford Worth. Considering its devices, this staff probably has a naval, rather than a constabulary provenance.

55. Constable's staff, 1809, wood, painted dark blue, with red, black and gold banding. Around the head, in gold, 'Gr.1809 Ph.' with, above, on a light blue-grey band, a crowned 'GIIIR' and the Royal arms in full colour. 530x43d. V3250 donated by Messrs C.& D. O'Donaghue.

56. do. 1830-7, wood, the upper section painted dark red with gold 'WR/IV'. The lower section is dark green, with a yellow tip, and is pierced for a thong. 569x37d Laycock 70.

57. do. c.1867, beech, the handle plain, with a white buckskin thong, the shaft being painted blue, with 'D' in red between red and white bands at the tip, and '2' below. 519x39d. V3240 no.757c used at the time of the Torquay Bread Riots. Donated by Mr W.H. Head.

58. do. c.1867, beech, the shaft painted dark blue, with 'B' between white bands at the tip, and '1' below, and pierced for a thong (missing) 550x43d. V3244 no.757a, from Torquay Corporation.

59. do. 'G' and '29'   557x42d.   V3246 no.7547d.

60. do.   'I' and '2'   512x41d.   V3245 no.757e

61. do. 'A' and '2' 508x39 V3242 no.757f

62. do. but in ash, 'K'(in red) and '3' 524x42d V3243 no.757g

63. do. as no.55, inscribed in white lettering 'E/21/TORQUAY BREAD RIOTS NOVEMBER 1867' no.2338. Donated by Mr G.A.Collins.

64. Truncheon, beech, unpainted, shaped as no.55.   530x43   V3247   no.757b. Donated by Mr J. Lane.

65. do. 1849, ash or hickory(?) shaft, varnished, and revolving on an iron rod secured in an ebonised handle, and stamped 'NO.1952 REGD 9 J1849/F.E. COLEGRAVE, BRIGHTON' 434x29d. no.2536 584/1938. Donated by the Rev. J.C. Carter Rendell.

66. Constable's rattle, beech, turned body and handle, two five-point ratchets vibrating two wooden strips secured by screws. 226x255x36 V3228 from A.H. Ogilvie.

67. do. varnished, and six-pointed ratchets 270x202x37 V3238 no.1423

68. do. similar to no.64, but with a U-shaped slot in the body, and the knob missing. 266x236x32 V81

69. do. similar to no.64, but with two lead plugs in the body, and one broken spring. 173x195x27 V82

70. do. similar to no.64, but with an iron plate holding the oak springs in place. 196x195x40 V1354

71. do. with ash(?) spring and ten-ponted ratchet 259x220x35.

72. Beech, with handle folding on its brass mount, the body stamped 'FIELD 233 HOLBORN' 'POLICE' and 'B381', and with two plugs of lead in the body, and a five-pointed ratchet 146x207x32 V1024 probably 378/1962. Donated by Mrs Holmes.

73. Handcuffs, iron, c.230x75x20 V3232 no.2893 found in a garden by and belong-

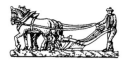

ing to Thomas Taylor, George and Dragon, Tansley, Derbyshire, on August 20th, 1903.

74. do. 1821? c.230x76x22 V3233 'carried by a policeman of 1821'. Donated by Mrs Swinson.

PUNISHMENT

75. Treadmill clock, iron movement, with provision on the right side for a drive shaft with a worm gear to operate the dial. White dial with black lettering, pine case with pale drab paint 320x129x355 no.1897 350/1936. Laycock 350.

76. Stocks, oak (?) with iron fittings and an iron key with a square socket in its end. 2165x585x570 630/1897 from Buckland Monachorum, donated by Rev. Preb. Hayne and the churchwardens.

EDUCATION

77. Slate, c.1875, blue slate in a rebated wooden frame stamped 'THE FLAG SLATE'. 166x10x223 used by Miss Toll at Cockington Primary School, Torquay, c.1875.

78. Tawse or strap, c.1870. leather, one end cut into eight strips 540x49 V3231.

COMMUNICATIONS

79. Bell (Town crier's?), bell-metal, secured to the end of an ash handle by an iron bolt 440x200d. V504 Laycock 76.

HOUSE STRUCTURE

80. Weather vane, early 20th cent. copper on a tubular iron pivot 691x753 Laycock 197.

HEATING, SOLID FUEL
FIREGRATES & FIREBACKS

81. Parlour range, early 19th cent., cast iron bases and front legs, the remainder being of iron bar and sheet riveted and bolted together 800x273x535.

82. Downhearth grate, wrought iron, riveted, 123x462x354 V603

83. Range, wrought iron, fire-welded 311x620x299 V604

84. Hanging firebasket, sheet iron with folded seam round base, rivets, and removable oval internal base 385x450x200 V1467 374/1936. Donated by L. J. Atwell. These items appear in Harrod's 1895 catalogue, p.284, at 1/9d or 2/6d each.

85. Fireback,1669, cast iron, 752x1256x49 Laycock 163.

86. do. early 20th cent. reproduction, cast iron, 609x568x32 Laycock 164.

87. do. 1700? cast iron, 828x570x15 Laycock 165.

FIREDOGS

88-89. Firedogs, early 20th cent. reproduction, cast iron, the long bars, inscribed 'ENGLAND', inserted into the uprights when they were being cast 441x397x248. Laycock 207(?).

90-91. do. late 18th cent., cast iron, 'CARRON' across the front 377x467x206. Laycock 210(?).

92-93. do early 20th cent.?, wrought iron, riveted, 348x745x226 V1537

94-95. do. wrought iron, riveted, 217x445x226 V1509 647/1898. Donated by Dr P.Q. Karkeek, who collected them from Trenchard.

96-97. do. wrought iron, riveted, 522x431x252 V602.

98-99. do. early 20th cent., wrought iron, riveted, stamped 'MILL & SONS' down the front of the uprights 309x398x68 V605.

100. do. wrought iron, riveted, 180x443x175 V606.

ACCESSORIES: BELLOWS

101. Pear-shaped bellows, elm, brass spout, leather flap valve behind a round hole in the back board 548x223 V571. Laycock 102(?).

102. do. but with woven leather over the hinge, 369x130 V1198 567/1970. Donated by Mrs D.I. Cole, Paignton.

103. do. but with conical sheet-iron spout, 608x248 V1527.

Wheel Bellows

104. cast iron base screwed to cast iron Corinthian column, and a cast iron drum, all painted dark green with yellow lining. Cast brass wheels, mounts and spouts, and turned beech handle. Four flat internal fan blades, 434x499x196d V1505.

105. Walnut boards, brass fittings, the drive band being tensioned by sliding the large wooden wheel backwards. Three flat internal fan blades, 174x543x92 at base V815 94/1932. Donated by Dr W.H.Kelson

106. Pine with tinplate top to drum and spout, all painted silver, then lined in black, with a dark brown scrumble. White ceramic knob. Four flat fan blades mounted on a square shaft, 181x401x137 V1136.

107. Elm with brass fittings and a copper spout. Turned round wooden handle beneath drive wheel. Four flat fan blades, 60x550x251 V1485 Fielden.

108. Pine and sheet iron, with two flat fan blades, 145x462x195 V1486.

Fire Irons

109. Log fork, wrought iron, 879x74 V770. This, or one of the other two-pronged forks, is Laycock 269.

110. do. 987x131 V769.

111. do. 885x110 V768.

112. do. 995x101 V1451.

113. do. 874x79 V766.

114. Poker, wrought iron, 830x19 V608.

115. do. 770x18 V607.

116. Rake, wrought iron, 803x93 V615.

117. Tongs, wrought iron, 704x97 V1174 574/1939 no.2477. Laycock.

118. do. 810x118 V614. Laycock 247?

119. do. 652x103.

120. do. 735x94 V616.

121. do. drop-forged iron, 243x80 V1175.

122. do. with a decoration of leaves and scrolls beneath the loops and down the sides of the blades, 259x66 V994.

123-24. Cinder shovels, cast iron blades inscribed 'A.Kenrick & Sons No.2' on the backs, 508x230 V1649 donated by L.E.Chapman, Torquay, June 1980.

125. Fire shovel, wrought iron, replacement blade fire welded to the shaft, 66x139x33d. knob V609 Fielden, from Court Farm, Maidencombe.

126. do. wrought iron, blade fire welded on to the shaft, 955x175x40d.knob V771 Warming Pans.

Warming Pans

127. Copper(?) pan fastened to iron frame with copper rivets. Brass lid, wire-edged, pierced and stamped, secured to wrought iron handle by a brass hinge, 1175x c.150x353d. V628I Laycock 11. Purchased by Mrs Fielden for £9 at the Laycock sale, Moretonhampstead.

128. do. 1165x c.140x306 V624.

129. do. brass pan and lid secured with a copper hinge and rivets to a wrought iron handle, pierced and punched decoration to the lid, 1157x c.115x324d. V626.

130. Spun brass pan and lid, fabricated ferrule, pieced and engraved decoration to the lid fastened with copper rivets to the hinge which is screwed to the oak shaft. Brass band on handle has a cast badge of a three-towered fortification with the motto 'SEMPER FIDELIS'. 118x c.100x308d. V627.

131. Spun copper pan and lid with pierced and engraved decoration. Fabricated ferrule screwed on to a polished wooden handle, 1055x c.100x320d V626. Laycock 83.

132. do. engraved lid and ebonised wooden handle, 1063x c.85x280d. V623.Laycock 82.

133. do. plain lid, 810x83x245d. V368 Donated by Mrs Morris-Williams, December 1984.

134. Warming pan, hot water, pressed sheet copper pan with copper screw-in ferrule on an ebonised wooden handle, 738x c.95x190d V632. Laycock 71.

135. do. pewter pan, with screw-in ferrule on polished walnut (?) handle. 1085x48x267d. V629. Laycock 82.

136. Hot water warming can, copper sheet, oval, wire drop handles at each end and central screw-top stopper, 597x c.400x c.120.

137. Pew warmer, sheet brass with spinning marks on the base, turned brass feet, and iron seating to the hinged side door. 191x192x158 no.2368. Laycock, from Cullompton.

138. 'Handwarmer', probably a shadow ball pierced brass sphere 117d. opening to reveal a three-ring gimbal holding a hemispherical brass lamp with a round wick, V929 no.2772 274/1941. Laycock.

LIGHTING, SOLID FUEL, STEELS AND TINDERBOXES

139. Steel striker,127x6 V651.

140. do. 90x51x8 V653.

141. do. c.68x38x4 V652.

142. do.,with two grips 94x46x3 V650.

143. Combined steel and tinder box, steel box with a hinged lid secured by a spring catch, which covers the container for the flint and tinder. The sides of the box act as strikers, 57x36x13 V565.

144. do. tinplate, black stove enamel exterior, with interlaced faded gilt border on lid. A steel striker is mounted under the lid, an oval liner has recesses for flints, and the base acts as a tinder box, 100x70x20 V566.

145. Tinder box, elm(?) nailed planks, charred around the upper chamber, 289x108x56 V907.

146. do. pine, nailed planks, heavily charred about its upper, loose-lidded chamber, 301x116x54 V567.

147. do., late 19th cent. sheet brass, soft soldered, with an engraving of a steam wing-powered airship taking off from an elevated platform, and the inscription 'Progress of Steam' 96x77x20 V1029. Fielden, from a Chagford farm.

148. Tinder box candlestick, late 19th cent.sheet brass, folded seams, with copper rivets to handle and candlestick 230x108dx69 V878.

149. do. folded seams, wired edges, copper rivets to handle, soft solder to candle stick 276x119d. x 102.

150. do. tinplate, folded seams, soft solder to candlestick, and tinder under internal damper plate, 109d.x85 V875.
151. do. 106d.x93 V553.

152. do. but neither damper plate nor rim to lid, 102d.x86 V878 no.2210 422. Donated by A. W. Galbraith

153. do. sheet brass, folded seams and soft solder, with internal damper plate 114x115x49 V103 and V910. Donated by Mr T. L. Harding.

154. Flintlock tinderbox, late 18th cent., steel with walnut stock, candle holder to left side. The door to the tinder box is stamped 'SAN.../HAMPTON', 163x37x56 to top of body V581.

155. do. late 18th cent., brass with steel lock and walnut stock, 194x59(legs)x61 to top of body V842.

156. Matchbox candle holder, sheet brass body with sheet iron interior, hinged ends opening to reveal (1) access to a candle and (2) a striking surface for matches, and a top lid to the match box 144x56x33 no.1774. Donated by W. K. Skinner, 'made by Thomas Wharton'.

157. Instantaneous Light Box. Tinplate, with folded seams and soft solder, red painted interior. The top and sides open to reveal a box for matches tipped with potassium chlorate, housing for a bottle of sulphuric acid with which they were ignited, and hinged candle stick 51x111x60 no.157 V861.

EMBER TONGS

158. Iron, brass rivets to spring, oval tips, 397x87x17 V1457.

159. do. 394x100x18 V1452 Fielden.

160. do. with pipe stopper formed from extended hinge pin, 384x102x18 V1183.

161. do. with pipe tamper on handle, 467x66x13 V1173

LAZY TONGS

162. Polished steel, 368x55 when extended. no.2439 V898.

163. do. 423x55 V900.

164. do. 492x87 no.2354 V899.

SPILLS

165. Spill holder, turned mahogany(?) 148x74d. V927 no.2172 485/1938. Laycock.

166. Taper holder, sheet brass with cast brass ring. The tube is slotted, with a sliding block to extend the woven taper as required, 527x20x7d. V906 no.2438 561/1939. Laycock

GRISSET PANS AND MOULDS

167. Grisset pan, cast iron, 298x237x141 V1011 no.1611 219/1934 from Mrs Burnett.

168. do. wrought iron, 520x353x77 V1278. Laycock 146.

169. do. 394x346x38 V549. Laycock.

170. Candle mould, tinplate,folded and soft soldered joints, 195x110x252 V538. Laycock 211.

171. do. 140x77x c.295 V908.

CANDLE BOXES

172. Walnut, nailed planks and brass hinges, 360x129x206 V526 no.2061. Laycock.

173. Sheet brass, folded and soft soldered, with stamped armorial on lid, 32x111d. V523. Laycock 30.

174. Sheet iron with black stove enamel, 342x98d. V938. Laycock 214A.

175. do. 375x108d. V940 Laycock 214B.

176. do. 353x120d V939. Laycock 214C.

177. Sheet brass, folded and soft soldered, 173x75x142 V1000 485/1938 no.2301. Laycock.

SNUFFERS

178. Iron, 163x62x9 V890.

179. do. with round finger loops, 157x50x9 V96 and V889.

180. do. with square box, 145x59x27 V893 no.1537 from Dartmoor. Donated by the Misses Hopkinson-Ash.

181. do. polished steel, 126x41x24 V892. Fielden

182. do. semicircular box, 138x44x24 V896 no.3173. Donated by Mrs Colmer.

183. do. oval box, 169x56x39 V538.

184. do. with spring, 143x43x19 at box, V888.

185. do. polished steel, with spring-loaded trap, stamped with a crowned 'WR' and 'PATENT', 181x56x40 V542.

186. do. polished steel, with cylindrical trap, stamped 'BRIGHT/SHEFFIELD' 156x48x47 V540.

187. Snuffer tray, sheet iron, black stove enamel, 231x104x16 V902 no.1537 from Dartmoor, with no.180.

188. do. with red, green and gold lining to the enamel, 238x92x16 V904. Donated by Mrs Bourne.

189. do. stamped sheet brass, 242x118x13 V903.

EXTINGUISHERS

190. Cast and turned pewter, 43x34d. V928.

191. Cast brass with wire ring, 63x32d.V543. Fielden.

192. Douter, polished steel, 112x56x25 V541.

193. do. 104x52x25 V895.

194. do. 115x55x26 V891.

195. do. brass, 142x59x18 no.2303 485/1938. Laycock.

RUSHLIGHT HOLDERS

196. Wrought iron, wall-mounted, 105x60x167 V929 390/1936. Laycock.

197. do. early 20th cent., 200x67x11 V28.

198. do. wrought iron, weighted, on oak base, 329x78d. V931.

199. do. on elm(?) base, 268x104x80 V530.

200. do. on tripod base, 273x150 triangular V934. Laycock.

201. do. 223x130 triangular V528.

202. do. 235x125 triangular V531. Fielden.

203. do. sprung, on elm(?) base, 295x115x101 V930.
204. do. on wooden base, 170x c.75d. V935 no. 2897.

205. do. on tripod base, 278x155 triangular V532.

206. do. 252x105 triangular, V386. Donated by Mrs Morris-Williams, December 1984.

207. do. sprung steel strip on turned elm(?) base 332x112 V932 Scottish?

208. Combination rushlight/candleholder, weighted, wrought iron on wooden base 242x c.84d. V924.

209. do. on oak base, early 20th cent. 282x97x103 V646.

210. do. on black painted modern(?) wooden base 195x112d. V889.

211. do. screwed with square nut on to tripod base, 687x330 triangular V535.

212. do. shaft riveted through base 880x295 triangular V778.

213. do. screwed to quadruped base with square nut, 1335x235 square V777. Laycock.

214. do. 1429x245 square V778. Laycock.

215. Combination rushlight/candleholder, weighted, hanging, wrought iron 488x125x19d V775.

216. do. early 20th cent. 787x127x25d. V602.

CANDLESTICKS, PRICKET

217. brass, cast and turned, shaft riveted through base 190x75d V925. Laycock.

218-19. do. grease cup screwed to base by pricket 314x80d. V537.

220. do. late 19th cent. iron, forged legs and pan secured by a tapered wedge through the base of the pricket. All upper surfaces are lightly engraved with foliage and scrolls 243x115d.x 145 V548. Laycock.

CANDLESTICKS, SOCKET

221. Turned oak 154x66d V833.

222. (Oven light?) copper sheet nailed on to wooden base 202x82x89d. V568.

223. Wrought iron, legs riveted through base 233x160d. V524.

224. 210x144d. V525.

225. Wrought iron, forged and riveted, with the pan screwed in place with a square nut 356x120x135 V557.

226. Wrought iron, spiral, on turned wooden base 238x c.19d. V562. from a Brendon farm, Exmoor. Fielden.

227. do. forged iron rod and stamped sheet iron, shaft riveted through base 156x113 V558. Laycock.

228. Wrought iron, hanging, 342x47d. V544.

229. do, but no drip pan 362x28d. V911.

230. do. sheet iron, screwed to base with square nut 198x105 V920.

231. do. 221x120d. V881.

232. do. two strips from shaft slotted through base 330x160d. V922.

233. do. folded and soft soldered seams, black stove enamel, weighted base 240x158d. V921.

234. do. but with shell shaped handle to

ejector and no drip tray 216x144 V556. Laycock.

235-6. do. sheet brass, spun base and brazed seam to shaft, drip tray and ejector missing, 169x104d. V914/1-2.

237. do. spun base, tubular shaft 158x90d V561.

238. do. 207x100 V915.

239-40. do. cast brass, 20th cent reproduction of 16th cent. design 178x87d. V546/1-2. Fielden.

241. do. oval, with central ejector, 152x109x82 V919.

242. do. rectangular base with central ejector 176x81x73 V918.

243-44. do. but no ejector 201x83x82 V916.

245-46. do. but with central ejector 309x116x115 V547/1-2.

247. do. 247x94x100 V917.

248-49. do. but no ejector 234x99x101 V913/1-2.

250-51. do, with telescopic column, and central ejector 172 to243x94x94 V882/1-2.

252-53. do. pewter, cast, stamped 'TC', a shield with a cockerel facing right, another facing left, and'X', beneath a cartouch with two triangles. Central ejector 193x96x74 V1230/1-2. Laycock.

254. Bedroom candlestick, tubular glass shield in a pierced sheet brass holder with cast brass handle and sheet metal and wire extinguisher 270x95d. V545.

255. Chamberstick, sheet brass, wired edges and cast candleholder, 82x202d. V877.

256. do. sheet brass, spun, brass rivets and soft solder, central ejector, stamped in oval cartouche 'ARMY & NAVY/C.S.L./MAKERS/LONDON' 132x320d. V570.

257. do. sheet brass, fabricated candleholder screwed to wire-edged base with an octagonal iron nut. Cast handle with copper rivets 53x143d. x245 V873.

258. do. sheet brass,pierced and soft soldered, cast brass handle 50x162d. V560. Fielden.

259-60. do. sheet brass, cast brass handle, with lidded matchbox and holder for an extinguisher. An embossed plaque beneath the candle holder has a 'TH' monogram 'TRADEMARK' and 'H. LOVERIDGE & Co. WOLVERHAMPTON' on a circular border. 48x169d. V879/880. Laycock 101.

261. do. pierced sheet brass with cast brass candle holder and handle with extinguisher 64x165d. V536. Fielden.

262. do. sheet brass with cast brass handle 127x186x178 V555. Fielden.

263. Pewter, stamped 'Z' '41' under base. The combined candle holder and extinguisher holder drop into a socket in the centre of the dish 52x 170d. V728/1. Laycock 224.

TAPERSTICK

264. Silverplate, fabricated from cast, stamped and rolled components, with light green coiled wax taper 134x119x92 no.2138. Laycock.

LANTERNS

265. sheet iron, soldered, horn panels, inscribed in white paint 'West Ropehouse/ Southfields' 550x203d. V1503. Collected from a cottage at Barton, Torquay, but presumably originally from the Southfield area of Paignton. Fielden.

266. Tinplate, folded and soldered, horn panels 520x209d. V1502.

267. do. riveted, iron suspension hook and boss, painted black outside and white within, horn panels 420x295d. V579. Laycock 20?

268. do. 540x295 V582. Laycock 61.

269. do. tinplate, folded and soldered, glass panels 421x184d V583 from a Chagford farm. Fielden.

270. do. 395x139d. at base. V576.

271. do. sheet brass, riveted, stamped and pierced decoration, engraved 'THE LIGHT

YOUR GUIDE', horn panels V577. Laycock 69.

272. do. sheet brass, folded and riveted, stamped decoration, horn panels and glass base 275x124x125 V575. Laycock 21.

273. do. tinplate, folded and wire edged, glass panels, turned and ebonised wooden handle 322x104x104 V936.

274. do. tinplate, soldered, glass panels, posts etc. covered in paper strips, traces of red paint 260x102x102. Laycock 63.

275. do. tinplate, soldered, painted black inside and pale green inside the door, wire mesh screen 273x115d. V527. Laycock. These are listed in Harrod's 1895 catalogue p.238 at1/2d each.

276. do. coopered oak spirit keg, converted by the addition of an oak top, horn panels and circular iron candle holder 343x205d. V580 380/1936. Fielden.

277. do. but with hipped oak roof and oval shaft, which is gripped by the carved hands of a supporting bracket lantern 480x175x180 from the Globe Inn, Exeter. Laycock

OIL LAMPS

278. Crusie, sheet iron 195x171x95 V563 no.1160 286/1936. Laycock.

279. do. 324x135x83 V564 no.1603 310/1935 from Guernsey. Donated by Guille' Alles Museum.

280. Betty lamp, sheet and wrought iron 285x100x73 V385 Donated by Mrs Morris-Williams, December 1984.

281. Oil lamp, wrought and cast iron 577x110d V550.

282. do. sheet brass, folded, soldered and embossed 192x65d no.2278.

283. do. clear blown glass, the brass wick holder which fits on top of the reservoir globe is missing 282x145d no.3407. Miss D'Anacker.

284. Bulls-eye lamp, tinplate, folded and soldered, with black stove enamel, internal round-wick oil lamp showing through a hemispherical lens 191x78d. V533. Laycock.

WATER

285. Well bucket elm, nailed planks with wrought iron bow handle swinging on two inverted V-shaped brackets 311x408x433 to rim V700 452/1964. From Hillside Farm, Cruss Orchard, Tiverton. Donated by R. P. Adams.

286. Water bucket, oak with iron bands, swing handle body 375x278d. at base V702.

287. do. 341x237d. V1325.

288. do. 365x229d. V1224.

289. do. side handle, branded three times 'JS' 350x236d. V1322.

290. do. no brands 244x266d. V1321.

291. do. 340x 274 V1656.

292. do. inside handle 380x280 V1320.

293. Dipper, copper on thick iron wire rim with tang extending to wooden handle 108x225d (see photo on p.14).

FURNITURE: STOOLS

294. Boarded stool, early 17th cent. (cf those made for the London Charterhouse in 1613. Chinnery p.262) oak, 496x600x192 V1596. Laycock.

295. do. mid 19th cent., walnut, 260x418x206 V1601. Laycock 289.

296. Joined stool, early 17th cent., oak, 541x512x290. Laycock 114.

297. do. 3rd quarter 17th cent., oak, 530x546x282 V1597.

298. do. late 19th cent, incorporating early 17th cent work, oak, 522x483x243 V679.

299. do. late 19th cent., oak, 594x455x263 V683.

300. Rectangular stool, 19th cent.,a batten is nailed across one end.elm, 402x415x235 V682.

301. do. 19th cent., each pair of chamfered tapered square legs is jointed into a

horizontal bar screwed up into the underside of the seat, elm, 326x360x240 V1707. Laycock 178.

302. do. 19th cent.?, oak, 295x444x248 V1705.

303. do. 19th cent.?, oak, 236x313x199 V1706.

304. Half-round stool, 19th cent.? the seat has a rounded front edge, and legs tapering from square to round. elm?, 390x464x259 V1600. Laycock 221.

305. Round stool, 19th cent.? oak?, 312x215d.   V681. Laycock 10? 'cricket stool'.

306. do. 19th cent.?, turned seat with turned legs, elm, 355x334d. V680. Laycock 177? 'round stool'.

307. Upholstered stool, late 18th-early 19th cent., the mahogany legs have reeded corners, into which are jointed beech? top rails veneered with mahogany. It is upholstered with a webbing base lined with striped ticking, horsehair, and blue striped chintz. Mahogany & beech? 386x404x302 V1598 . Laycock 287.

308. Footstool, mid 19th cent.,pine, nailed planks with four turned feet, upholstered top covered in formal cross-stitch design, sides covered in dark brown twill 150x289x289 V787 . Laycock 107.

CHAIRS

309. Comb-back windsor chair, c.1740-80, elm seat, ash legs and sticks. The legs are roughly squared and chamfered, two being repaired by driving in nails to stop them sliding up through the seat. The sticks are wedged under the seat and secured into sockets in the comb back by handmade nails driven in from the back, the same method being used in the arms at each side of the central stick and in the front arm sticks. Evidence of dark green paint all over, except for the legs and the underside of the seat. (see Cotton p.27) elm & ash, 958x575x347 back 545w. Laycock 124.

310. Comb-back windsor chair, c.1750-1780, elm seat with ash legs and sticks, all the joints being through morticed and wedged (no wedges in the comb). There are

pegs through the outer stick/comb joints, and handmade nails through the seat/stick joints and the second and fourth seat rail/stick joints. Originally unpainted, there are traces of corroded black varnish on this chair. 'K' is incised on the back of the right arm. Elm & ash, 822x 538x336 back 446w. Laycock 123.

311. Round-seated comb-back windsor chair, late 18th cent.,elm seat with beech sticks, ash/ arm supports and beech top rail. Most of the oak? two front legs are original, the rest being restored when a wooden X-frame beneath the seat, together with iron leg-stays, were being inserted. The arm supports, two back sticks and the legs are through-jointed, the remaining joints being blind mortices. Both the back sticks and outer sticks are secured by wooden pegs inserted through their joints. Elm & beech, 815x426x524 back 441w. V1774. Laycock 118.

312. Side chair, birch with black paint, 838x 396x396 back 445w. Laycock 120.

313. Comb-back windsor chair c.1750-1780, elm seat with scratch-moulded bead around its upper perimeter. Beech(?) sticks and legs? The outer comb/stick joints have round pegs driven through them, while the joints between the sticks and both the arms and the seat in the middle, at the bottom of the back and at the ends of the arms, have square pegs. The beech arm supports are morticed and wedged into the seat, and nailed to the arms. The stretcher construction is all blind morticed. Elm & beech, 1038x654x465 back 634w. V1775. Laycock 122.

314. Bow-back windsor chair, c.1870, elm seat, back arm rail and arm supports, ash legs, arms and bow and beech sticks. The arm rail is in three pieces halved together, the arm supports are morticed through the seat, and all the underframe, leg and seat joints are all blind morticed. The tops of the sticks are tapered with a draw-knife where they are blind-morticed into the bow. 'U.ALSOP' is stamped upside down on the back of the seat, indicating that it was made by Uriah Alsop (c1830-c.1900) at his Broadmead works, Bristol. (see Cotton p.5). Elm & ash, 1049x372x473 back 522w V1777. Laycock 121.

315. Wheel-back windsor chair, late 19th

cent elm seat with beech frame and sticks, iron braces added to the front legs and under the stretchers. Blind mortices throughout, except for through mortices at the top and bottom of the turned arm supports. 'J.A' is stamped upside down on the back of the seat. Elm & beech 1128x481x439 back 515w. Laycock 116.

316. do. elm & beech 1121x481x439 back 515w. Laycock 126.

317. Bow-back windsor side chair, late 19th cent., beech? seat, ash legs, bows and sticks. The rails and legs are glued into blind mortices, the stick/bow and bow/seat joints are through mortices, the latter being wedged. There are traces of an all-over coat of dark green paint. Beech? 870x347x373 back 431w. V1729. Laycock.

318. do. but with 'G Par(s?)' scratched on the front of the top of the bow. Beech? 867x340x375 back 423w. V1728. Laycock.

319. Windsor rocking chair, late 19th cent.? elm seat, legs, machine-turned sticks, etc, ash bows (and rocker?). Blind mortices throughout, except for through mortices at the bottom of the arm supports, and nailed joints at their tops. Half-round blocks added to the ends of the arms to produce scroll terminals. All-over dark brown stain. 'B' stamped upside down on the back of the seat elm and ash 1200x513x502 back 516w, rocker 776l.

320. Joined armchair, c.1730, pegged mortice and tenon construction, black oilcloth upholstered seat oak, 1238x631x454 back 464w. Laycock 125.

321. Joined armchair, early 19th cent., pegged mortice and tenon joints throughout, arms repaired with screws. Dark red/brown paint over dark green paint. Elm, 813x486x409 back 464w. Laycock 119.

322. Upholstered chair, c.1900, slab back with glued and screwed legs and rails all stained dark oak colour. Seat and back upholstered with petit-point panels of red, pink and white roses, buds and foliage, with machine-made silk braid secured with dome-topped brass upholstery nails around the perimeter. Oak, 1059x490x470w.

BENCHES & SETTLES

323. Bench, oak top and ash legs. Scarred by frequent chopping at one end, and some at the other. One leg is incised 'W V'. Oak and ash, 529x2674x237 (seat) 460 (legs).

324. Settle, early 19th cent.?, reed-edged tongue-and-grooved planks, the seat halved into the ends, and nailed, oak 1710x1367x310 V1778. Laycock 167.

325. Bacon settle, early 19th cent?, joined construction, door furniture and hinges, late 19th cent. replacements, elm, 1778x1805x558 (seat) 205 (cupboard). Laycock 166.

326. do. mid 19th cent.?, tongue-and-grooved plank construction, the curved back incorporating a full-height cupboard entered by two pairs of double doors in the back. Elm, 1800x2120x485 (seat) 180 (cupboard). Laycock 168.

TABLES

327. Table, four planks, each secured to its neighbour by five morticed and pegged loose tenons. Top, oak, 48x2602x875 Laycock 154. Frame, rectangular legs, chamfered inner corners, rounded external corners, with pegged mortice joints to receive the rails. One end is framed for a drawer (missing). Oak, 770x2178x750. Laycock 153

328. Tripod table, mahogany, fixed rectangular top with rounded corners, on turned column 654x637x730h.

329. do. mahogany, circular tip top on turned column 700h.x517d. Laycock 155.

CUPBOARDS

330. Corner cupboard, hanging, early 20th cent., oak front, the door being made from late 17th century? panelling, the remainder made up from old timber, all mounted on a tongue-and-grooved pine carcase. Oak and pine, 1194x832. Laycock 158.

331. do. bow-fronted, late 18th cent., oak with mahogany crossbanded doors and top and bottom mouldings, brass escutcheon and H hinges. Inside, four shelves, with two drawers beneath the lowest 1047x515 radius. Laycock 160?

332. Corner cupboard, early 19th cent.,top cupboard with three shelves with ornately-shaped front edges, the bottom cupboard having a single straight-fronted shelf. All the original paint surfaces were stripped in the 1980s, but Laycock photographs show it with a dark painted surface chipped in places to reveal a light (drab?) coat underneath. Pine, 2015x1310. Laycock 156.

333. do. early 19th cent., pine, with dark painted exterior. The upper section has a pair of ten-light doors and two internal shelves, the bottom section having a pair of panel doors and one shelf 2004x986 maximum diagonal. Laycock 157.

WASH STAND

334. Wash stand, mahogany construction, with oak dovetailed drawer linings and brass drop handles to each drawer. Mahogany & oak, V1518 314/1961. Donated by Mrs M. Dix.

CHESTS AND BOXES

335. Boarded chest, 17th cent., plank construction, staple hinges, and internal till with reeded lid on right hand side. Oak, 548x922x344.

336. do. with framed front, 17th cent., oak, 176x643x435.

337. do. 17th cent., nailed construction. The lid originally hinged on battens turning on pegs forming an integral part of the back panel, but was fitted with iron strap hinges at some later date. Oak, 298x732x279. Laycock 9, 179 or 201.

338. do. c.1680, nailed construction. New hinges, feet and an oak patch replacing the original lock, are all late 19th – early 20th century. Oak, 235x595x347 V1606. This, or no.44, may be either the original no.2958 which was purchased by Mrs Fielden at Laycock's sale for £1.5s.0d, or be Laycock 9, which she purchased for £8.4s.0d.

339. do. late 17th cent., nailed construction, iron strap hinges and lock, hasp missing. Oak, 178x472x309 V1604. Laycock 9, 179 or 202.

340. do. early 19th cent., dovetailed corners with nailed-on bottom and a pine till along the top right of the interior. The underside of the lid is inscribed in brown ink 'John Fletchers/Box' . His brand, a conjoined 'JF' is burnt into the centre of the lid. Oak and pine, 210x446x321 V644. Laycock 9, 179 or 201.

341. do. 1749, red lead on all internal surfaces, except for the renewed back panel. The exteriors of the front and sides are decorated with black paint in reverse silhouette, with a pair of birds (peacocks?) on the front and floral sprays on the sides. The underside of the lid is inscribed in brown ink '...Lee His Box 1749' 'Elizabeth ...her box 1773' 'John Lee His Box 1789' between the iron strap hinges. Pine, 97x333x236 V832 no.697A. Donated by J. Worth, Torquay, 29th Jan,1985.

342. do. late 17th cent., nailed construction with butterfly hinges. Three varnished oak drawers inserted inside and late 19th – early 20th century battens screwed to the underside of the lid. Oak, 283x498x375.

343. do. on stand, early 19th cent., pine, plank construction, on joined stand. Dark brown painted exterior. Laycock 171.

344. Salt box, 19th cent., nailed construction, nailed leather hinge. Elm, 438x320x261. Laycock 98.

345. do. 19th cent., oak, with elm back and pine drawer linings, nailed construction. Brass drawer knob secured by an hexagonal iron nut. Oak, elm & pine, 369x251x137 V726. Laycock 23 no.2330

346. do. 19th cent., nailed and glued construction, highly polished exterior, and brass hinges, walnut, 372x190x122 V388 donated by Mrs Morris Williams, Dec.1984.

347. Knife box, early 19th cent., dovetail corners, with a sliding lid decorated with mahogany cross-banding and 'MH' inlaid centrally in square black wooden pegs. Beech, mahogany and ebony? 410x122x78 V864. Laycock 96.

348. do. early 19th cent., dovetail corners, nailed-on back and sliding lid. Mahogany, 480x117x88 V812. Laycock 122.

349. Spice box, mid 19th cent. five internal divisions radiating from a central cylinder containing a grater, tinplate, black japan varnish, gilt banding and brass handle

93x155d. V1763 484/1965. Donated by Miss M. Green.

350. do. mid 19th cent., tinplate, as no.54, but with an embossed 'WS' and compass trade mark soldered under the lid, and no handle, V31/1 85x148d.

351. do. mid 19th cent. four birch? drums which screw together to form a single column, each bearing a rectangular label for 'MACE', 'GINGER', 'CINNAMON' and 'ALL-SPICE', all beneath a glossy varnish. Birch? etc. 206x94d. V381. Donated by Miss Morris-Williams Dec. 1984.

352. do. mid 19th cent., birch? as no.56 but with four drums for 'MACE', 'CINNAMON', 'CLOVES', 'NUT-MEGS', 181x81d. V1384 no.2355 517/1935. Donated by C. Laycock.

353. Flour tub, mid-late19th cent., oak with ash bands with lap and nailed joints, 338x394d. V649. These are listed in Harrod's 1895 catalogue, p.205 priced from 2/9d to 6/9d.

354. Teapoy, early 19th cent., rosewood, lid opens to reveal central section with two cylindrical cut-glass bowls flanked by removable hinge-lidded rosewood caddies lined with zinc paper. 800x445d. From A. H. Ogilvie.

355. do. early 19th cent., mahogany, lid opens to reveal a central velvet-lined recess for a glass bowl (missing) between two removeable hinge-lidded caddies 804x410x309.

356. do. mid 19th cent., rosewood, rectangular body on polygonal shaft on rectangular base. Lid opens to reveal two hinge-lidded caddies lined with zinc paper 770x455x410. Donated by A. A. Ogilvie.

TEA CADDIES

357. c.1800 oak, burr walnut veneer with box(?), harewood(?) borders and a marquetry oval lily-of-the-valley panel to the front. Inside, single compartment with mahogany lid and turned ivory knob. 122x95x121.

358. do. c.1780 wooden carcase, rectangular with broad chamfered corners, all edges rosewood veneer, all other surfaces are covered in floral patterns of scrollwork in red, blue and green papers gilded on the edges, green twill on base. Inside, divided into two paper-lined compartments. 122x98x195.

359. do. early 19th cent. pine, mahogany veneer, box and cross-banded borders, ivory escutcheon, brass ball-and-claw feet. Inside, two hinge-lidded mahogany caddies (one missing), inside of lid lined in red paper, with zig-zag boxwood/rosewood marquetry border. 304x154 no.2443. Made by Mr George Mayne of Wanslow, Berks, as a present to his bride. He died in 1867 aged 78. Donated by his grandaughter, Margaret B. Dockray.

360. do. early 19th cent. boxwood banded corners and diagonal cross on lid, ivory escutcheon, brass lion-mask ring handles at each end, brass ball feet, and green paper on base. Inside, two foil-lined compartments with ivory knobs to boxwood lids, and a central red-marbled paper lined compartment with a wheel-cut glass bowl. On a bone label inside 'Rev. J. Blackmore's Tea Caddy'. He was curate at Tor Mohun before 1850. Mahogany etc, 165x306x151 V? no.2945 donated by Mrs Joce, 747/1943.

361. do. boxwood banded corners and kite-shaped escutcheon. Green baise on base. Inside, two foil-lined compartments with turned ivory knobs to lids and a central baise-lined compartment for (missing) glass bowl. Mahogany etc, 145x305x148 V377. Donated by Mrs Morris-Williams, Dec.1984.

362. do. inlaid round brass escutcheon and turned wooden feet. Inside, two foil-lined compartments with small turned ebony? handles to lids. Top lined with red paper. Mahogany, 137x248x128 V378. Donated by Mrs Morris-Williams, Dec.1984.

363. do. brass ring handle on foliate mount on lid and brass ball feet, the bottom covered in dark blue paper. Inside, two foil-lined compartments, division and lids missing. The top is lined in red paper. Mahogany, 139x191x114 V379. Donated by Mrs Morris-Williams, Dec.1984.

364. do. nailed boarded construction with lid fitting into dovetail slides cut into the side panels. Black lacquer exterior with gilt line borders to each side and top, and Chinese characters on the top, back and front. Red paper lining with red block-print pattern. Pine, 270x263x265 V1603.

365. do. tinplate, folded and soldered, with black japanning 158x114x81 V1001.

366. do. tinplate, folded and soldered, printed in black with interlace design with oriental figures and 'HARTLETT BRISTOL', with oval chromo-lithograph female portrait head applied to the front, all clear lacquer. 163x82x82 V949.

367. do. tinplate, stamped, folded and soldered, printed with black figures etc around the sides, all clear lacquered, and stamped on the base 'BRYANT & MAY PATENTEES/LONDON'. 160x94d hexagon.

CRADLES

368. Cradle, North Fresian? mid 18th cent., framed construction, the rocker section being removable from the base by means of a central peg joint. (cf. H. J. Hansen, European Folk Art (London 1968) pl.58c. Oak, 383/1936 no. 1978. Donated by C. H. Laycock as a 'Jacobean Cradle'.

369. do. late 19th cent. framed construction. The general form of this cradle is very similar to that found in Austria and Switzerland, although the carving is similar to that of late nineteenth century English 'Jacobean' reproduction woodcarvers. It is probably an English reproduction of a continental piece. Overall dark oak stain. Oak, with sheet lead lining. 965x700x600.

370. do. late 19th cent. frame construction, dark-stained wood carved with 'Hush a bye baby...' around the rails. 905x813x540.

371. do. frame construction, mahogany, with turned bobbins and slatted base 924x725x762.

372. do. dovetail plank construction, pine, with external oak graining and internal white paint. V427 1004x572x675.

CLOCKS

373. Longcase clock, early nineteenth cent?, oak, mahogany cross-banding and veneer to the glazed door, pine back-board, and gilt caps and bases to the columns. The white dial with date ring, the spandrels painted turquoise-green with yellow and blue pansies, green leaves etc.and the dial painted 'Peter Waycott, Paignton'. Oak, mahogany, pine, brass & iron,

1973x470x241 no.2503. Donated by Mrs A. H. Ogilvie. This maker is also recorded in late 18th – early 19th cent. at Holne, Ashburton and Totnes, where he apparently made the movements, cases, and painted the dials of his clocks.

374. do. oak with mahogany cross-banding and pine back board, early 18th cent. Brass dial with single hour hand, cast brass face-mask spandrels and the inscription 'W. Clement, Totnes'. Oak, mahogany, pine, brass & iron, 2085x578x287. W. Clement was working in Totnes in 1700, was mayor in 1711, and died there in 1736.

375. do. oak with mahogany cross-banding, gilded gesso caps and bases (now painted black) to the columns. Brass dial with date ring etc, two false winding holes, and cast brass spandrels showing an urn between two eagles. Oak, mahogany, brass & iron, 1970x460x V373. Presented by Mrs Morris-Williams, Dec. 1984.

376. do. movement only, cast-iron front plate inscribed 'FIN MORE/& SON'. The white dial has 'Conway Castle' painted on its top panel, abbey ruins in the spandrels, and the painted inscription 'Wm. Davy, Tavistock'. Bell missing. Brass, iron etc. 430x34 V1634. Laycock 88. William Davy, clockmaker, is recorded in the Tavistock directory of 1856.

377. American clock, pine carcase with mahogany and rosewood veneer, the glass door having an imitation etched glass lyre design. The eight-day movement has a recoil escapement, no alarm, and a white dial with two winding holes. An ornate paper label inside the back has a rich border with an American eagle and text including; 'EIGHT-DAY/CLOCKS/Manufactured by/BREWSTER & CO/BRISTOL, CONN. U.S.A./Directions for Setting.../BENHAM, Printer/ Globe Building/Cr. Church & Chapel Sts. E. Haven'. Pine, mahogany, rosewood, brass, iron, etc. 425x110x76 V1646. Laycock 16.

378. do. pine carcase with rosewood? veneer and the glass door painted on the reverse with fruit, blossoms and foliage in natural colour on a white ground. Movement with recoil escapement, white dial with inner brass alarm disc, and a domed iron bell. Inside the back a blue paper label states 'CHAUNCEY JERSEY/MANUFACTURER

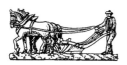

OF/EIGHT AND ONE DAY/BRASS CLOCKS/ TIME PIECES,AND MARINE CLOCKS/NEW HAVEN,CONN./U.S.A.' Pine, rosewood?, brass, iron, etc., 369x189x93. Laycock 75.

379. Clock case, pine carcase with mahogany veneer front, the glass door with a formal silver pattern on a blue background. Movement missing, but white dial with pairs of green leaves painted in the spandrels. Pine, mahogany, glass, iron etc. 284x180x89.

380. Bracket clock, oak carcase with rosewood veneer and brass inlay, and a pierced brass gothic window lined with red silk at each side, beneath ring handles on lion-mask mounts. Brass ball feet. The movement has a gothic arch-shaped frame engraved with a border pattern. The white dial has a strike/silent lever at the top, the painted maker's name being worn away, although the place name 'COLCHESTER' remains. Oak, rosewood, brass, etc. 439x264x159 V1632.

381. do. walnut with walnut veneer, brass handle and ivory knob to door. The white dial, with separate seconds dial, and the spandrels painted with sprays of pink and blue flowers with foliage. Walnut, brass, iron etc. 535x287x197 V1640.

382. Watch pocket, c.1810-15 mahogany with bone inlaid edges, 'door', feet, drawer edges and diamonds in each side panel. The watch pocket is lined with red paper. Mahogany and bone, 315x171x103 1055/1929 no.737. Made by French prisoners of war at Princetown. Donated by Rear Admiral O'Dogharty.

383. do. early 19th cent., mahogany on pine block, 294x103x94 615/1940 no.2744. Donated by W. H. V. Walters.

BIRD AND SQUIRREL CAGES

384. Bird cage, late 19th cent., wickerwork, 600x505x495 V1681. Laycock 94.

385. Fowl cage, late 19th cent., wickerwork, 725x490d. V729 Laycock 174.

386. Squirrel cage, mid 19th cent.,pine, with thin varnish, and iron wire cages, handle, staple hinges, catches and handles. There are traces of c.1840s wallpaper stuck beneath the base. White opalescent glass knob and tin tray. Pine, iron wire, tinplate etc. 387x582x268 V724. Laycock 173.

387. Birdcage, mid 19th cent?, pine with pine rods pierced through the rectangulaR frame, and a sliding tin plank in the base to act as a door. There are two perches and a feeding trough. pine etc. 190x192x153 V728 Laycock 95?

388. Birdfeeder, galvanised iron plate construction, with four feeding holes, a tray in front, a pair of wire suspension hooks, and a hinged lid opening to reveal two hoppers glazed to the front. An embossed oval plaque reads 'J. ABRAHAMS/NATURALIST/ PATENT'. Iron plate, glass, etc. 134x142x72 V844. Laycock 42.

PATCHWORK QUILTS

389. Silks, cottons, flannels, woollens etc.,with striped, checked and damask weaves, prints etc. Each four-inch square has a central diagonal square, two borders, and four triangular corner pieces. c.1990x1520 531/66 V2161. Donated by Mrs E. Walter.

390. Mainly silks and velvets, each six-inch square having a central square surrounded by five overlapping borders and a backing of plain, checked or printed cotton. c.1550x1720 531/1966, 69/1953 V2182. Donated by Mrs E.Walter

METAL ORNAMENTS

391-92. Lion & Unicorn, mid 19th cent., pewter, lion 153x143x29 unicorn 139x146x29 V1234/1 & 2 no.2369. A & B. Laycock collection.

393-94. Peacocks, mid 19th cent., pewter, 113x68x25 119x69x24 V463/1 & 2.

395-96. Pheasants, mid 19th cent., brass, mirror-image pair, 113x68x25 119x69x24 V463/1 & 2. Laycock 150.

397-98. Pheasants, mid 19th cent., brass, with solid backs, secured with two iron screws on to separate bases, mirror-image pair, 94x95x27 92x96x26 V458/1 & 2.

399. Wheatsheaf, mid 19th cent., brass, base screwed to base with iron nut, 184x103x43 V457.

400-401. Greyhounds, mid 19th cent., brass, mirror image pair 104x147x29 99x142x29 V455/1&2.

402-403. Retrievers, mid 19th cent., brass, mirror image pair, 66x177x26 62x173x27 V459/1&2.

404-405. Plough teams, mid 19th cent., brass, mirror image pair, with two cast brackets at back for screws into base. 97x228x25 100x236x24 V464/1&2. Fielden collection, one is Laycock 81.

406-07. Stallions, mid 19th cent., bell-metal, mirror-image pair, fastened to bases with two square iron nuts, 236x287x54 226x288x55 V471/1&2. Laycock 418 no.2154,1937.

408-09. Stallions, mid 19th cent., cast iron, mirror-image pair, 197x298x35 199x297x35 V470/1&2 no.2333 509/1938. Laycock collection.

410-11. Equestrian figures, brass, '...M.STANLEY' 155x117x29 'MAJOR RAPT...' 154x177x28 V460/1&2.

412-13. Miniature candlesticks, late 19th cent., brass, turned shaft on square hollow cast base, 85x42x42 V884/1&2.

414. Miniature candlestick, late 19th cent., pewter, stamped 'TC','X' etc. on base, 70x40d. V887 447/1937. Fielden.

415. Miniature tip-top table, mid 19th cent., brass, cast and turned base, floral engraving on top, 72x65x55 V1101.
416. Miniature brass fender, cast brass

GLASS ORNAMENTS

417. Witch ball, clear, faintly green blown glass ball, the interior spattered in red, yellow, green and blue paints before being coated with white paint. 120d. V365.

418. do. hung by a black bootlace from a wooden toggle slipped through the top hole, 130d.

419. do. clear royal blue glass, 80d V366.

420. do. hung with a black thread from a wooden toggle slipped through the top hole, 105d.

421. Clear glass, silvered interior, rosette-pattern iron cap pierced by a splayed iron split pin for suspension, 70d. V364.

422 .Snow scene, late 19th cent., clear glass ball with a model red-roofed church on a mound inside, partly filled with water and 'snow', all mounted on a moulded black glass base 100x72d.

423. Scene, late 19th cent., clear glass ball with cast yacht sailing in front of an over-shot watermill, all mounted on a rectangular alabaster(?) base. 65d.x 84h. V290.

424. Walking stick, mid 19th cent., pale green glass, twisted shaft and hooked handle, 980x87 194/1934. Donated by Miss Pengelly.

425. Miniature top hat, mid 19th cent., dark olive green glass, pontil mark on base, 71x92x88.

426. Pipe, mid 19th cent., pale ruby clear glass, 425x58d. at top of bowl V383. Donated by Mrs Morris-Williams, Dec.1984

427. Rolling pin, mid 19th cent. slightly green glass, 464x540 V820.

428. do., the interior flecked with red, yellow, green and blue colour, backed with white paint. 410x68 V820.

429. do.,opaque white glass, with dark brown transfer prints of:

a) THE GREAT EASTERN STEAMSHIP',
b) GOD SPEED THE PLOUGH,
c) *'When this you see remenber me*
And bear me in your mind.
Let all the world say what they will
Speek of me as you find'
d) *When tempests mingle sea and sky*
And winds like Lions rage and roar
Ships o'er the mountain waters fly
And down unfathom'd depths descend
Though skill avail not strength decay
Deliver us good lord we pray.
e) A sailing ship. 827x101d. V825.

430. do. with worn transfer print of two figures to the left and a sailing ship to the right, flanking a central cartouche HOME ACROSS THE SEA... 350x 63d. V821.

431. do. painted inscription 'A/Present from/Cardiff' flanked by a pair of sailing

ships overpainted in blue, green, red and yellow. 410x60d V819.

432. do. remains of paper panel and dark red borders. 375x48d. Donated by Mr Selwyn Oxley.

433. do. print of the *Great Eastern* picked out with red on a green sea 'Tonnage 22500Tons THE GREAT EASTERN STEAM SHIP Length 891 Feet Breadth 118 Feet'. 359x60d.

434. do. clear blue glass, with gilt prints picked out in red
a) Brig,
b)   *Sweet O'sweet is that sensation*
        Where two hearts in union meet,
        But the pain of separation
        Mingles bitter with the sweet.
c) LOVE AND BE HAPPY,
d)   *When far at sea remember me*
        And bear me in your mind.
        Let all the worldsay what they will/
        Speak of me as you find.
e) COME BOX THE COMPASS. 755x88d. no.2328

435. do. slight remains of red picking out. 748x86d. V823.

436. do. gilt prints picked out with red and green
a) SCHOONER
b)   *When far at sea remember me...*
c) COME BOX THE COMPASS. 410x66d

437. do. gilt and red painted 'Remember me' 321x44d.

438. do. gilt painted decoration
a) around an engraving on paper of two sailing ships
b) 'For my Mother',
c) crossed Union Jacks with red crosses. 344x51d. Donated by Mr Selwyn Oxley.

439. do. clear purple glass, gilt prints picked out in red and green
a) MARINERS ARMS
b) 'The Gift... (very worn verse),
c) NORAN CRE...STEAM YACHT
d) Sweet O,sweet is that sensation...
e) sailing ship '...FROM HULL' 718x92d. V824.

440. do. Nailsea type with white flecked dark green glass and a convex profile 396x54d.

441. Glass doorstop, green glass, blown with single internal flower in a pot 95x87d. no.2193 Laycock.

442. do. double flower 100x66d. no.2138 Laycock.

443. Alum Bay sand glass, glass, filled with a representation of Alum Bay executed in sands collected there and the inscription 'Alum Bay Sand I.Wt' and 'R(?). Lawrence (Fecit?). On the base a label reads 'The whole/of the/ PROCEEDS/ arising from these/Ornaments/ will be given in Charities/These COLOURED SANDS are/all taken from Alum Bay/Isle of Wight/ Price...s.d.' on yellow paper. Glass & sand etc. 194x62d.

444. Ship in bottle, Three-masted ship, rigged but without sails, and painted red and white, with the name .S. BLANCA', against a background of model houses, a church, lighthouse and a windmill. 230x102d. V818.

445. do. but with no name on ship 304x74d.

446. do., four-masted ship, rigged but without sails, painted black and white, on a blue and white sea. bottle moulded with 'C.S.& Co.',' 261' on base 232x103d.

447. do., four-masted ship, rigged but without sails, painted grey and black, against a model of houses, neck enclosed by a woven cord seal. 313x71d.

448. do., three-masted ship rigged, but without sails, painted black, against a background of houses, a church, lighthouse and two windmills, neck sealed with red wax 236x83d.

449. do., two three-masted sailing ships rigged with sails and painted black, these being the 'Avelon' and the 'Rose Marie', sailing on a blue and white sea, the neck of the square bottle is sealed with a heraldic design in blak wax 242x135h.

450. do., three-masted sailing ship rigged with sails, plain wooden hull, named the 'Sligo', in an oval bottle 243x91x56.

451. do., three-masted sailing ship rigged without sails and flying the Union Jack, a single-masted yacht sailing in the opposite

direction and has 'No.P.6.'on its sail. There is a model lighthouse at the bottle neck. There is a five-pointed star seal on the neck 335x118d.

452. do., three-masted ship in full sail, black and white hull, the neck houses a long tapering wooden plug, tipped with a cross-piece with brass bead terminals 295x80d.

453. Ship in case, three-masted half-model vessel in full sail,black and white hull, being approached by a steam tug, all on a painted sea and sky within a glazed gilt-framed box 305x233x82 no.3608. Donated by Mrs A. F. Brooke

454. Ship in case, three-masted fully rigged model ship, without sails, but flying the red ensign, mounted on a stand within a mahogany case glazed to front, back and-top. 444x326x175. Laycock 91.

455. Ship in case. The 'Inch-Garvie', a vessel with two masts for sails, and a funnel painted black above and red below a row of white diamond shapes 767x443x210 Laycock 33.

SHELL ORNAMENTS

456. round panel with a broad border of shells enclosing a glazed frame showing shells and seaweed before a print of a yacht in full sail. The back is lined with wood-grained paper bearing a MADE IN ENG-LAND' stamp and '17/6' 202dx43

457. as above, but with a print of Grace Darling beneath a convex glass. 203dx55 V1032.

458. Shell box, cardboard with lid and bottom lined with blue paper mounted with shells and a convex satin oval on top. The sides are covered in yellow diapered paper, the base in wood-grained paper stamped 'MADE IN ENGLAND' 237x158x105. Collected by Mrs Fielden as a locally-made souvenir.

PRISONER-OF-WAR BONE ORNAMENTS

459. Guillotine in bone, rectangular base guarded with six soldiers and having a pair of gates leading to stairs to an upper level. Here, guarded by four soldiers, is a body with its neck beneath the triangular axe which slides in its vertical grooves.

364x78x190 no.2580. Laycock. Made by French prisoners of war at Princetown, Dartmoor.

460. Crucifixion scene, 1806-8. Bone, with painted decoration. An accompanying letter states that this was presented by 'Mrs Fleming (Cumbernauld...) ...made by French Prisoners of War at the Gaol at Princetown 1806-7-8. It was bought by Mr Scobel of Penzance for his sister-in-law Mrs Kitty Stevens of Chieveley, Berks, who left it to her great neice, Mrs Fleming. The figures... were carved from the bones saved by the prisoners from their meals'. no.2586 597/1939. Laycock.

STAFFORDSHIRE FIGURE ORNAMENTS

461. 'Dick Turpin' on horseback, facing left, 284x169x63 C645.

462. 'Dick Turpin' on horseback, facing right, 230x134x52 C644.

463. 'Tom King' on horseback, facing left, 287x168x64 C643.

464. 'Going to Market' boy and girl on horseback, facing left, 206x134x47 C649.
465. 'Returning Home' boy and girl on horseback, facing right, 207x132x48 C648.

466. 'Duke of Cambridge' on horseback, in uniform, facing right, 223x123x48 C650.

467. 'Sand Woman' standing with her donkey, which faces right, 233x236x115 C774 323/1936. Donated by Mrs W. E. Fielden

468. 'Ruth' gleaning, with corn, 368x135x115 C657.

469. 'Rebeckah' at the well, a pair with no.160, 370x155x113 C658.

470. 'Rebecca at the Well', a female figure at a well, giving a man a drink from an ewer, both figures being in eastern dress. A hollow tree stands above the well. 267x155x81 C652.

471. 'Red Riding Hood' seated figure with the wolf, 146x97x68.

472. 'Prince Albert'? standing in dress uniform, 178x67x65 C659.

473. 'Babes in the Wood' at either side of a hollow tree, with a bird on the ground between them, 135x89x65 C664.

474. Girl standing against a wall on which stands a beehive, all under an arch of flowers and foliage, 180x95x95 C665.

475. Scotsman? a figure in a kilt and plaid, holding a duck in his left hand, a shotgun in his right, and a spaniel at his feet, 310x127x86 C656.

476. Girl seated by a tree stump, holding a rabbit? 138x89x59 C622.

477. Man in 18th century costume standing by a wicker flower basket with grapes and vine leaves, 232x73x80 C653.

478. Girl standing in front of a large sheep which faces left, 227x C769.

479. Scotsman with sheep standing in front of a large sheep which faces right, a pair with no.170, 208x122x56 C770.

480. Youth standing by a cow which faces right, 156x134x75 C763.

481. Milkmaid sitting at the right of the cow, holding her bucket with both hands, 156x189x95 C764.

482. Girl standing to the right of a hutch, which stands on a wall, together with two rabbits, 140x70x49 C690.

483. Boy in tunic, cravat and sash, mounted on a horse with a saddlecloth, 275x157 90x75 C646.

484. Girl girl in bodice, skirt and hat, on horseback, with a lamb close by, 278x158x74 C647.

485. Girl on goat facing right, 123x102x44 C747.

486. Boy on goat facing left, a pair with no.473, 124x102x43 C748.

487. Girl on goat facing left, 167x118x55 C749.

488. Boy on goat facing right, a pair with no.475 167x C750.

489. Girl rides a goat, facing left, a boy

stands at the goat's head. Both figures are in 18th century costume. 165x113x41 C663.

490. Two huntsmen standing with a deerhound, 300x158x66 C642.

491. A man, with a spaniel under his left arm and holding a girl with his right, both within an open-work bower, 296x203x87 C651.

492. A girl holding a basket and a man holding a swan, 210x112x58.

493. A girl to the left holds a sheaf of corn on her head, while a man to the right holds a water jar, 318x177x72 C655.

494. A man standing on the left, with a woodwind instrument, and a girl to the right, by a cross-barred gate, holds a tambourine, both being in 18th century costume, 192x123x55 C660.

495. A kilted man stands to the left of a pump, holding a jug on top with his left hand, while an ewer below collects the water. A girl sits to the right, 270x147x63 C654.

496. Three Victorian female acrobats wearing caps, bodices, skirts and drawers, all perched on marble steps, the central figure on a stool at the top, the others on both sides on the bottom step, 233x67x65 C661.

CHIMNEY ORNAMENTS

497. An ecclesiastical gothic facade, with a central door, traceried windows and steep gable between two crenelated turrets, 219x173x86 C678.

498. do. a lighthouse, 124x112x88 C689.

499. do. a lighthouse, cottage and rowing boat with two figures, a girl and a boy with a hamper, 165x134x87 C670.

500. do. a mansion with a central round tower topped by a conical roof and chimney, flanked by two wings, 163x126x59 C685.

501. do. tall house of irregular shape, clad in vines, a dovecote on the roof, and a boy and girl standing in front, 236x195x60 C687.

502. do. cottage ornée with a dog in its central porch, 190x120x96 C686.

503. do.a swan in a stream, surmounted by a brick arch, above which a ballerina performs in a bower to the accompaniment of a youth with a stringed instrument. 140x70x49 C691.

504. do.a cottage, with its walls pierced by a door and two front windows, and with a gabled window in the roof, all on an oval base, and decorated with flowers and foliage, 124x112x88 C688.

505. do.a symmetrical house with its central roofed porch flanked by two shallow domed roofs, 180x185x66 C684.

WATCH STANDS

506. Tall group, with three figures in 18th century costume, a girl kneeling on the left of the watch, a boy on the right, and a boy sitting in the open-work branches of a tree overhead, 305x146x68 C673.

507. do. gabled watch stand, with female figures to each side, and a third kneeling between them, 284x210x70 C674.

508. do. the watch is set in a gothic facade, between slim turrets and above a central door, 225x220x64 C667.

509. do. watch set in a fruiting vine, between a seated girl with a sheep, and a standing man with a woodwind instrument. There is also a spaniel at their feet, 298x170x66 C671.

510. As no.506 except for minor variations in colouring, 320x182x71 C672.

511. do. watch set in a turreted gothic manor house. The central door is flanked by two pools with swans, and side doors, 258x123x67 C676.

512. Watch stand/candle holder. A girl on the left, and a boy to the right, both in 18th cent. costume Scots dress, accompanied by a goat and a spaniel, 234x123x67 C675.

513. Mock watch stand with painted clock face, the dial set in a hollow tree flanked by a boy and a girl who are holding up a bunch of grapes. They both stand on a two-arched bridge over a river, 203x114x54 C680.

514. do. the dial is set beneath a bird of paradise, and is flanked by a girl to the left, and a boy to the right, 164x110x52 C682.

515. do. the dial has a vine above, a vase below, a girl to the left, and a boy to the right, both holding baskets of grapes etc. 322x181x73 C679.

516. do. the dial has flowers above and below, with a girl to the left and a boy to the right, both in eighteenth century dress, 173x106x44 C683.

517. do. the dial is set on top of the shallow pediment of a symmetrical facade, flanked by flat-topped turrets, and with five door-ways at ground level, 190x185x76 C681.

SITTING SPANIELS

518-19. do. mirror-image pair, 295x305 x120 301x305x120 C694 C695.

520-21. do. mirror-image pair, 325x206x92 340x202x95 C696 C697.

522-23. do. mirror-image pair, 331x204x96 337x198x96 C698 C699.

524-25. do. mirror-image pair, 252x186 x108 257x182x102 C700 C701.

526-27. do. mirror-image pair, 227x190 x135 231x186x123 C702 C703.

528-29. do. mirror-image pair, 217x162 x105 220x160x104 C704 C705.

530-31. do. mirror-image pair, 167x131x94 175x126x87 C706 C707.

532-33. do. mirror-image pair, 148x119x69 155x110x60 C708 C709.

534-35. do. mirror-image pair, 145x135x77 154x129x77 C710 C711.

536-37. do. baskets of fruit at their feet mirror-image pair, 164x99x65 165x 99x64 C712 C713.

538-39. Two spaniels sitting besides a barrel, and one on a barrel 107x41x77 108x36x77 101x77x37 C716 C717 C718.

540. Two spaniels flanking a barrel 206x153x61 C741.

542. Sitting spaniel facing right 90x73x39 C720.

543. do. 89x66x47 C721.

544. do. 132x94x62 C722.

545. do. 91x72x39 C723.

546. do. 91x91x38 C724.

547. do, 86x62x33 C726.

548. do. 85x54x30 C727.

549. Sitting spaniel facing left 73x55x33 C719.

550. do. with a basket in its mouth 105x69x48 C725.

551-52. Standing spaniels, mirror-image pair, 122x125x57 129x128x36 C734 C735.

553. Spaniel and puppy, both sitting, 139x118x77 C742.

554-55. Sitting dalmations, mirror-image pair, 111x87x60 132x87x58 C714 C715.

556-57. do. with puppies lying in front of them, mirror-image pair, 73x 76x C728 C729.

558-559. Greyhounds, mirror-image pair, 30x 27x C732 C733.

560-61. Standing greyhounds, mirror-image pair, 248x 253x C736 C737.

562. Lying greyhound facing left, 92x123x43 C738. Donated by Miss Loveridge.

563. Standing greyhound with a rabbit in its mouth 145x142x48 C739. Donated by Miss Loveridge.

564. Mastiff lying under hollow tree,148x137x73 C743.

565. Sitting cat facing right, 180x105x76 C744.

566. Cockerel, 102x44x37 C745.

567. Cow, 60x73x35 C746.

568. Cow creamer with lid, 119x168x79 C751-2.

569. do. 119x154x86 C753-4.

570. do. 132x168x87 C755-6.

571. do. 123x168x80 C757-8.

572. do. 126x159x78 C759-60.

573. do. no lid, 138x 165x73 C761 Laycock.

574. do. 144x187x75 C762.

575. Stork and fox, 127x75x75 C765

576. Lying sheep,facing right in front of a hollow tree, 122x112x78 C766.

577. Lying sheep, facing right, 58x84x42 C767. Donated by Miss Loveridge.

578. Sheep,facing right, standing in front of a hollow tree, 122x109x68 C768.

579. Two sitting poodles flanking a hollow tree, 135x120x66 C771.

580. Sitting giraffe beneath two palms, 144x102x63 C722.

581. Standing giraffe in front of a hollow tree, 169x112x48 C773.

CERAMIC WALL PLAQUE

582. White earthenware with black transfer print 'PREPARE TO MEET THY GOD' and pink lustre. Sunderland pottery, early-mid 19th cent. Laycock.

OIL PAINTINGS

583. Seascape, 1755, showing The *Buckland* complete, wrecked, and temporarily repaired, as described in three narrative panels painted against the sky:

'The Buckland Wm Bartlett of St Mary Church Owner & Commander Sail'd from St Johns Newfoundland the 5th of Novr 1755 Bound for Torbay in Lat 49 No. Long 28D 60M West of the Lizard A Gale Came on Novr 16th When Scudding Under Her Foresail & Double Reef Top and Sprit sails at 1/2 past 7 P,M Ship'd A Sea Which Left her as in Draft 2nd Which Carry'd Away all our Masts Bowsprit Boats Windlass Pumps & Swept the Deck Broke her Beams Wash'd Overboard 11 Men & Kill'd 1 Part of our Cargo 7 Feet of Water in the Hold Lost all our Sails & Riging Except the Fore Shrouds We Lay too

*from Sunday to Tuesday When We Raised
Jury Mast & Foresail Wore Ship Wind
West Steer'd as in Draft 3rd we were
Towed 30 Hours by the Ambuscade Frigate
44 Guns.*

*The Men Drowned were Malachi Harvey
Wm Codner Mate Elias Shears James
Lavis Wm Stowlake John Davis Auth Tarr
John Shapley Rich'd Evans Tho's Splat
PhilP Turner the latter Killed with the
Beam Robt Cole of St Mary Church had
his Leg Broken By Gods Providence Arived
in Torbay Decr 9th And Shall Always
Remember the Old 5th of Novr.'*

in a dark painted moulded frame with gilt
inner border, 680x1580x45. Donated by
J. S. Bartlett, 1884.

584-86. Three views of Torquay from the
sea, c.1800?, which form a continuous
panorama from
a) Waldon Hill to the Fleet stream (now
Fleet Street),
b) The Strand and
c) Park Hill and the original quay (now
Victoria Parade) showing the early harbour
before its reconstruction in 1803-5 by
Robert Palk. All are in pine frames with
quarter-cut oak veneer, c.436x605. Donated
by C. B. Oak.

CUT-PAPER SILHOUETTES

587. Black paper, deer in woodland,
198x125 no.1536. Donated by the Misses
Hopkinson, March, 1929.

588. do. fighting cocks, 67x123 prov. as
no.579.

589. do. a thrown horseman, 105x50, in
rosewood frame with gilt slips, 213x195x22
V127. Fielden.

590. do. a thrown horseman, 106x64.
Donated by Miss Laurie Newman.

591. do. a lady on horseback for which a
dismounted man picks roses from a bush.
Burr maple frame backed with newspaper
dated 1866. no.2265 217x281x22. Donated
by Mrs Tyers.

592. do. a couple in a cart having their
donkey frightened by one boy standing on
his head and another, jumping on the back
of the cart, sounding his rattle. no.2264
218x281x22 a pair with no. 591.

PIN-PRICK PICTURE

593. Paper, a woman and small girl with a
drum, within an elaborate floral, shell and
trellis border, with flower, trellis, drum and
grass picked out in watercolour, all in a contemporary moulded pine frame with gilt
inner border, the backing paper being dated
1808. 350x252x23 no.2142 V3165. Made
by Mr King's grandmother who lived at
Modbury about 1800.

SAMPLERS

594. 'Susanna Rouse Worked/This in The
Years 1743'. Blue thread on linen backed
paper, lower case alphabet and the poem
'How Doth the little Busy Bee...' with
crowns and hearts filling the lines and a
border of trees etc. across the bottom.
310x211 no.2250. Donated by the Rev. J.
C. Carter Rendell.

595. 'Margaret Drewe Her Work Uffculm
Augus 1778' Coloured thread, silk and
crewel on linen. Two alphabets in caps., a
scroll border of pinks?, nos.to23, a scroll
border of roses?, then, surrounded by floral
sprigs:

*To Day Man's Dress'd in Gold and Silver
    bright,*
Wrapt in a Shroud before to Morrow Night,
To Day he's feeding on delicious Food,
To Morrow Dead, and nothing can do good.
*To Day he's Nice, and scorns to feed on
    Crumbs;*
To Morrow he's himself a Dish for Worms
To Day he's Honour'd, and in vast Esteem;
To Morrow not a Beggar values him.
To Day he rises from a Velvet Bed;
To Morrow lies in one that's made of Lead.
*To Day his House, tho' large he thinks but
    small;*
To Morrow, no Command, no House at all.
To Day he's Forty Servants at his Gate
*To Morrow scorn'd not one of them will
    wait.*
To Day Perfum'd, as sweet as any Rose,
To Morrow stinks in every Body's Nose.
To Day he's Grand, Majestick, all Delight,
Gashful and Pale, before to Morrow Night.
*True as the Scripture says, Man's Life's a
    Span*
The present Moment is the Life of Man.
Of Life the present Moments all we're sure,
*We can't call back one past, nor one to come
    insure'*

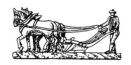

in a glazed mahogany frame with gilt inner moulding 378x284x18. Laycock 142.

596. 'Mary Luscombe her Work Finished May 2 1803 Halberton'. Coloured silks on linen, scroll border with 8-petal flowers, floral sprigs and a pair of birds, a large spray of pinks, lilly of the valley, roses etc. tied in a bow, and at the bottom Adam and Eve, the Tree of Knowledge and the serpent, between pairs of lions and flowerpots, all mounted on a mahogany board. 548x422 no.2253 463/1937. Laycock.

597. 'Frances Layton Her Work In The Years 1811'. Coloured silks on linen, a scroll border with flowers, two very worn verses ending with 'Let me then make God my Friend' and 'And on all his ways attend', then a basket of flowers between two flowerpots, more flowerpots, and then a house, with two birds on the roof, a tree within railings at each side, a stag and a dovecote etc. all in a mahogany cross-banded mahogany frame, the back-board inscribed 'Glass fixed on June 18 1911 A. J. Willey Otherwise as purchased' 349x348x22. Laycock 143.

598. 'ELIZABETH WALTER HER/ WORK IN THE/ NINTH YEAR/OF HER AGE/ 1822'. Coloured threads on linen with paper backing, single line border, triplicate alphabet of caps., repeated numbers to 19, then single to 26, then:

'Our hearts are fasten'd to this World
By strong and endless ties
But every sorrow cuts a string
And urges us to rise'

318x220 no.2185 434/1937. Donated by Miss E. R. Graham.

599. 'Mary Ann Paul Finished This Work/ October 27 Aged 11 Years Anidomena 1824'. Coloured thread on linen, lower case alphabet, nos. to 11, alphabets in caps, then lower case, numbers to 9, and:

'Hosanna to King David's Son Who reigns on a superior throne. We bless the Prince of heavenly birth Who brings salvation down on earth. Let evry nation evry age In this delightful Work engage. Old men and babes in Sion sing The growing Glories of her King August The 31'

then trees, dogs, flowerpots, birds, and a stag. 542x202 no.1447. Donated by Mrs A. P. Daniel.

600. 'EMLA HOLE/ CHAGFORD May/ 24th 1830'. Coloured silks on linen, border of small triangles, two doves, and a large wicker basket full of flowers, all in a glazed black (originally gilt) frame. 195x144x16. Given by A. H. Ogilvie.

601. 'Sarah Wills Finished This Sampler July 11th 1836'. Coloured silks on linen mounted on board, scroll border with pinks? and

'Deceiv.d by subtle snares of hell
Adam our head our Father fell
When satan in the serpent hid
Propos.d the fruit that God forbid'

The main elements comprise a house, Adam, Eve, the Tree of Knowledge and the serpent, an angel, and various birds, squirrels, lions, foliage and flower pots 460x333 301/1961. Donated by Mrs W. H. White, Torquay.

602. 'Elizabeth Little Aged 9 Years 1837'. Mainly green with some red thread on linen backed with paper, scroll border with flowers, a repeated alphabet of caps., numbers to 7, a lower case alphabet, numbers to 6, an alphabet of caps., birds, dogs, trees, flowerpots across the bottom. 387x315 332/1961. Donated by Miss G. E. Pearse.

603. 'Caroline Punchard/ Torquay, June 10, 1852'. Pale pink thread on linen, of alphabet repeated caps. and numbers to 10, a lower case alphabet, the year in Roman numerals, then:

'The fear of the Lord is the beginning of knowledge, but fools despise wisdom and instruction. The Lord giveth wisdom: out of his mouth cometh knowledge and understanding. Her ways are ways of pleasantness, and all her paths are peace'

292x219 1052/1929. Donated by Mr Hanson.

604. 'Fanny Shaw Ag'd 9 Years' [1852]. Coloured thread on linen, broad blue and grey chequer border, alphabet of repeated caps., numbers to 17, a lower case and italic alphabets, then:

'Ask not wish not to appear
More beauteous rich or gay
Lord make me wiser every year
And better every day'

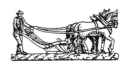

all in a glazed dark wood frame 332x370x14 no.3705 78/1953. Donated by her daughter Miss E. A. Godley.

605. 'Sacred.To.The./Memory.of./ William. Johnson.Who.Died./ Januery.1.1854.Aged. 12/years'. Mainly black and coloured crewels on linen, border of leaves, beneath the inscription are four birds, then a monument 'Sacred', a tree and a church. 353x399 no.1559. Part of a collection made in mid 19th cent. Lancashire. Given by the Rev. Burgess to the donor, Mr Watkins.

606. 'Jane Smalley/ Aged 11 Years 1868'. Dark blue thread on linen, border, alphabets in caps. and lower case, numbers to 10, alphabet in italic caps. 230x227.

607. 'Martha Louisa Snellgrove 10 Years/ Redbridge National School 1876'. Red thread on linen, narrow border of small florets, alphabet in caps.,numbers to 14, alphabet in italics, then lower case, in caps. and lower case once more. 187x188 no.3066 826/1946. Donated by Mrs Stratford Cox.

608. 'JANE COWELL VALLENCE'S/ work done in the eighth year of her age'. Coloured silks on linen with linen backing on pine board, a rich floral border around a wicker basket of fruit, grapes etc. and:

O thou the dispenser of the good we possess,
Let the infant before thee, thy goodness
confess:
In grace and in mercy, thy blessing impart,
Let the name of my Saviour, be wrote on my
heart;
That while with my needle, my time I
employ;
May my thoughts rest on Heaven, the place
of all joy'

375x334.

609. 'Emma Lampard aged 13 years/ Worked at Lady Byrons School Kirby Mallory August 16'. Coloured threads on linen, border of shaped panels enclosing coloured crosses, at the top a pair of doves, a spray of flowers between a pair of birds in foliage, then an octagonal cartouche of blue and yellow flowers surrounding:

'See the kind shepherd Jesus stands. Thus
I may safely venture through. And calls
his sheep by name. Beneath my shepherds
care. Gathers the feeble in his arms. And

keep the gate of heaven in view. And feeds
each tender lamb. Till I shall enter there'

At the bottom, a spray of roses etc. between two peacocks on foliage and a boy and a girl in contemporary costume, all in a glazed pine frame grained as burr maple. 526x428x31.

610. 'Fanny Larter Aged 8 Years'. Coloured threads on linen, simple zig-zag border, an alphabet in caps.,nos. to 10, a lower case alphabet, a row of birds, dogs and plants, and a final alphabet in caps. 287x 371 no.1914. Donated by Miss Larter.

611. 'SUSANNA PETTMAN GROTTO HOUSE MARGATE APRIL 26'. Brown thread on linen, simple zig-zag border, the names of all the counties of England and Wales from north to south in caps. 189x294.

612. 'Sarah E A Salmon'. Blue thread on linen, single line border, two repeated alphabets in caps. one in lower case. 282x280 no.3067 826/1946. Donated by Mrs Stratford Cox.

613. 'Isabella Ann Mann Stevens Finished this sampler in the ninth year of her age'. Mainly blue and pink thread on linen, single line border, three alphabets in caps., nos. to 36, a lower case alphabet, then:

'Remember now thy creator in the Days of
thy Youth Honour thy Father and mother
Obey your teachers in all their commands'

numbers to11, plants, cowns and initials in the lower corners 400x429.

614. 'Mary Wedden Standard IV Shiphay Collaton National School'. The above is written on the backing paper of a sampler worked in coloured thread on linen, a border with small florets, an alphabet in caps., nos. to 9, a basket of flowers, and a lower case alphabet. 305x250.

615. Anon. Purple, blue and brown thread on linen, single zig-zag border and one alphabet in caps. Unfinished. 565x458.

616. Anon. Coloured silks on linen, a rich border of green foliage with blue and yellow flowers enclosing:

'They that go down to the sea in ships,
that do business In great waters These see

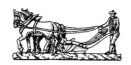

the works of the Lord, and his wonders in the deep PSALM CVII Ver:23.24.'

beneath two butterflies, a three-masted ship in full sail, with a ship's boat to the left, and a small yacht to the right, all in a glazed rosewood and boxwood cross-banded pine frame. 465x336x28.

617. Anon. Coloured thread on linen, a circular border with a central green parrot surrounded by two pairs of birds, flower pots, rosettes etc., all in a glazed oak frame. 201x187x25. V1103.

618. Anon. Coloured thread, mainly green and white, on linen, a zig-zag border, with a central bird in a cage, within a swag of foliage, between two flying birds and two birds on bushes, all in a glazed black frame. 117x168x12 no.1912 V125. Donated by Miss Larter.

619. Coloured woolwork on linen, a grey, fawn and dark brown tabby cat beneath a tasseled brown drape, all in a moulded black frame. 211x299x20.

620. do. A pink border with a scroll of flowers, surrounding a black, white and tan tabby cat sitting on a red carpet decorated with green and yellow crosses, all within a glazed plack painted pine frame. The back board inscribed '...Wood/ January 1846 Friday Night' 342x336x36. Laycock 141.

621. Coloured woolwork kettle holder, a floral wreath and the Gothic capitals M and G all on a black background, with a black woollen backing and hanging loop. 133x153 V1124.

MAINTENANCE

622. Fire bucket, leather with copper rim and rivetted construction. 249x295d no.1966 no.374. V1668. From Tor Newton House, Newton Abbot. Donated by L. J. Atwell.

623. Housemaid's box, red painted pine, nailed construction, with iron corners and handle. 185x372x270 V846.

624. Knife board, pine, faced with camputicon, an embossed brass label reads 'THE WELLINGTON KNIFE BOARD/OAKEY'S KNIFE POLISH' and a red advertising label on the reverse, 450x145x22 V868.

625. Emery stick, oak coated on both sides with an emery compound, the handle stamped 'S.LINLAY...', 450x53x15 545/1968 V869. Donated by Miss Crump.

626. Knife Cleaner, ash, cast iron, brass etc., manufactured by George Kent, 199 High Holborn, London, with patent improvements 1870, 1882 and 1887. 480x500x230 372/1962. Donated by Mrs M. Freeman.

627. Wash-board, pine, nailed construction, with corrugated brass rubbing surface. The wood is stamped 'NORTHERN QUEEN/ BRITISH MADE' 598x310x51 715/1993 V1769. From The Priory, Abbotskerswell. Donated by Mr Blunt.

628. do., marked '10/6' V1769 598x305x51.

629. Posser, spun copper stamped 'WAFAX TRADE MARK', on pine handle. V781 790x204d.

FLAT IRONS

630. Cast iron with wrought shafts to sheet iron handle 120x154x97 V956.

631. Cast iron with polished wood handle, the iron cast 'SENSIBLE NO.6 N.R.S. & CO.' 88x100x49 567/1970 V567/1970. Donated by Mrs I. D. Cole.

CHARCOAL IRON

632. Cast brass with iron hinge pin and oak handle 219x259x162. Laycock.

BOX IRONS

633. Cast brass with iron billet. 65x91x37 V1551.

634. do. with turned shafts and turned wooden handle 128x160x85 V951.
635. Cast iron with turned wooden handle, 2 iron billets, 121x100x72 V957.

636. do. beech handle, 1 billet, 161x144x94 V966.

637. do. wood handle, 1 billet, 168x150x99 V952.

638. do. 150x132x86 V1552.

639. do. 158x142x96 V154.

640. do. with sheet iron hand shield, brass face and billet, 164x162x110.

IRON STANDS

641. Sheet brass with copper legs, 36x250x105 V1565. Laycock.

642. Cast brass, 34x218x96 V1588.

643. Wrought iron, through riveted, wood handle, 38x259x112 V964.

644. Cast iron, chromed surface, 42x292x98 V963.

ITALIAN IRONS

645. Cast and wrought iron secured in originally red painted wood base with lead plug, inserted brass eye. 202x192x88 V1561. Laycock. Probably Scandinavian.

646. Cast iron on wrought stand, 237x170 x160 V1553. Donated by A. H. Ogilvie.

647. Cast iron, base cast '13', wrought shaft, 183x151x117 V958. Fielden.

648. do. cast '11' and 'C.F. Co.' (i.e. Carron Foundrey, Falkirk) 175x137x105d V959.

649. do. 141x162x104d V1731.

650. do. with iron slug, 140x100x89d V1554.

651. do. 113x105x84d. V1549.

652. do., base cast 'KENRICK', slug with wooden handle, 109x63x70 v1550.

653. do. rectangular base 150x (base) 106x83 V1548.

654. Cast iron, turned shaft secured with square nut, 236x163x112 V1560. Laycock.

655. Cast brass, turned shaft secured with square nut, 191x153x108d.V1546. Fielden.

656. Turned brass secured to polished iron base with hexagonal nut, 295x117sq. V1547. Fielden.

LUMP HEAD

657. Cast iron on wrought iron shaft riveted through base, 227x135d V1559. Donated by C. Shapley.

CRIMPING BOARD

658. Sycamore? 20x101x138 V1564. Laycock.

CRIMPING MACHINES

659. Iron, double screw, brass, wooden handle and elm base, 270x320x264 V1114. Donated by Mirs Sanders 1937

660. Iron and brass, 190x324x149 V961.

661. Green painted iron, single screw, brass, on oak base, 350x308x215 V1545. Laycock.

662. do. 245x335x160 no.1047.

663. do. 219x3129x130 with iron slug.

FLY TRAP

664. Blown clear glass 183x132d. Donated by G. Rayler 1969.

DEADFALL MOUSE TRAP

665. Oak, screw construction, 220x306x 110 V1594.

HOLDING: MEAT FORKS

666. Wrought iron with copper inserts.

667. Wrought iron, wood handle, 445x47 V996.

668. Wrought iron with red leather thong, 424x87 V852.

669. Wrought iron, beech handle, 298x74 V853.

670. Wrought iron, wood handle, 270x34 V995.

671. Wrought iron, 540x59 V767.

672. do. 497x73 V1178.

BEATING: STEAK BEATER

673. Beech, 345x89x65 V13.

BREAKING: SUGAR CUTTERS

674. Steel, 256x84 V993.

675. do. 239x70 V990.

676. do. 218x73 V91.

677. do. 225x79 V 90.

678. do. 201x80 V991 From a Chagford farm. Fielden.

679. do. 237x81 no.383/1962 V987 Donated by F. L. Goldthorpe.

680. do. one leg straightened to replace the spiggot, 251x80 no.51/543.

681. do. 232x95 V992.

682. do. mounted on a baseboard.

Chopping: Cleavers

683. Iron/steel, turned beech handle, 246x64 V851.

684. Iron/steel stamped 'GHA/ 2', and with paper label writen 'sent me by Mr White of Bridgetown... probably a... ' V1292.

685. do. remains of wood handle in ferrule, indistinct stamp on blade, 334x64 V1289

Chopping Knives

686. Iron/steel, wood handle with brass screws 138x158 V1007.

687. do, ash handle on iron shafts, 179x144 V835.

688. do. beech handle, shaft stamped 'BRADES CO' 195x126 V1465.

Grinding: Mortars

689. Bell-metal, 110x128d. V1488.

690. do. 112x130d. no.1925 356/1936. Donated by Miss Norman.

691. do. 122x 149d. V941.

692. do. 63x94d. V947.

693. do. 88x111d. no.1925 356/1936 V948. Donated by Miss Norman.

694. do. 126x151d. 'WG 1712' V1558 Laycock.

695. Brass, turning rings on base, 140x151d V946.

696. do. 100x125d. V1473.

697. do. 94x120d V1575.

698. Bell metal, 92x95 V945.

699. Cast iron, 220x243d. V655.

700. *Lignum vita*, 183x184 V1332. Laycock.

701. White marble, 172x264 no.2118 V654. Donated by A. H. Ogilvie, 1937.

Pestles

702. Bell metal, 214x37 V942

703. do. 174x34 V942

704. do. 120x20 V945

705. do. 195x35 V1558

706. Brass,. 183x31 V1575

707. do, 181x31 V1473

708. do. 237x40 V946

709. do. 148x24 V943

710. Iron, 275x59 V655

711. *Lignum vita*, 320x70 V1332

712. do. 360x87 V654 Donated by A. H. Ogilvie,1937.

Grating: Nutmeg Grater

713. Tinplate, folded and soldered, 187x62 V987.

Pressing: Tongue Press

714. Tinplate and galvanised cast iron, solid plunger and removable pierced baseplate body 171x 155d. V1488. In Harrod's 1895 catalogue, p.235 these cost 4/- each.

Lemon Squeezers

716. Beech? five holes in bowl, 275x55 V857.

716. do. with iron hinge, 229x55x42.

717. Cast iron, cast 'PAT APR 7 1868' on lid, with removable white porcelain cup and bowl, 227x82d V982.

Vegetable Presses

718. Tinplate, soldered, 65x144d. V852.

719. Beech, 127x223d.

Mixing

720. Bowl, Verwood pottery, internal lead glaze, 108x270d. V1280.

721. Spoon, beech, 520x94 V1034.

722. Egg whisk, tinplate and sycamore?, 476/1965 V998. Donated by Mrs Morris Williams.

Moulds

723. Charlotte, copper with tinned interior, 103x214x128 V980.

724. do. 75x78x135 engraved with D beneath a coronet.

725. Ornamental, do., 110x188x126 stamped '945', V972.

726-27. do. (pair) 92x144x104 V969.

728. do. 130x115d. V975.

729. do. 142x125d. stamped '467' V970/1.

730. do. identical to no.728, 132x125 V970/2.

731. Dariole, do., 44x50d V981.

732. do. 48x54d. V974.

733. do. 48x51d. V973.

734. Icecream bombe mould, tinplate, soldered, 218x124d, V968.

Straining/Sifting: Dredgers

735. Spun brass, 106x68d. no.2119 1937/404 V1556. Laycock.

736. do. 112x72d. V1526.

737. do. 73x49d. V837.

Cooking Supports: Branders

738. Wrought iron, riveted construction, 290x650x391 V666.

739. do. riveted through side bars, 317x260x54.

740. do. six round and one flat bar riveted through side bars 610x464x38.

741. do. legs riveted through rectangular top frame, 198x338x263 V668.

742. do. legs fire welded under triangular top frame, 169x238sides V1013. Laycock 237.

743. do., similar to no.328, 167x302sides V1615.

744. do., legs fire welded on to top ring, 155x195d. V630.

745. do., similar to no.330, 194x170d. V589.

746. do. 242x275d. V590.

747. do. 176x216d V597.

748. do. early 20th cent.,similar to no.330, but made of round iron bar, 169x142d. V1269.

749. do., wrought iron, with three internal spikes formed by the upper ends of the legs fire welded (two on top, and one beneath) the top ring, 159x175d. V593.

750. do., but all legs fire welded on top of the ring, 157x256d. V594.

751. do., but forged from round bar, 189x252 V592.

752. do., but with the short legs forged out horizontally at the base to give greater stability, 46x291 V591.

753. do. with parallel bars rivetted beneath the top ring, and the legs socketed from beneath and riveted over, 300x304d V1647.

754. Wrought iron, the end turned down to form the third leg and so ensure stability, 216x582x215d. V584.

755. do., with three legs riveted through the top ring and handle. Three of the top spikes were fire welded in place, one being replaced with a riveted spike, 190x568x245 V746.

756. do., two spikes forged from the inner end of the handle, the round legs all being socketed in from below and riveted over, 136x470x136   V747

757. do., two front legs turned out as feet at the bottom, and inward as leaf-shaped spikes at the top, after being fire welded over the ring. The third spike extends back as a handle, with third leg socketed through it and riveted over, 429x178x174   V1591.

758. do. V531.

759. do., the two front legs extended back across the ring to form a cross shape. The end of the handle turns down to form another leg, a fourth leg being socketed into the handle adjacent to the ring and riveted over, 532x188x120 V600.

760. do., with cross of bars under the ring, and three legs, 587x285x194 V596.

POT HOOKS

761. Wrought iron, fire welded,   850x100 x24 V1531.

762. do. right handed 970min.x1309 max.x96 V1178.

763. do. 1055 min.x 1407max.x94.

764. do. 1156 min.x 1698 max.x101

765. do. 824 min.x 1144 max.x86 no.2586 from the Old Manor House, Stoke Gabriel.

766. do., handle missing, crook 748x120 x29, rack 764x90x50

767. do. 930 min.x1275.max.x88 V1534.

768. do. 1105 min.x1407 max.x105 V766.

769. do. 110 min.x1608 max.x109 V755.

770. do. 1214 min.x1608 max.x90 V1536.

771. do. but the hook is round bar, 775 min.x1209 max.x83 V759.

772. Rack and hook, left handed, wrought iron 106 min.x1414 max.x95 V757.

773. do. 900 min.x1235 max.x86 no.2791 from Combe Cottages, Stoke in Teignhead, 1940.

774. do. 738 min.x1084 max.x87 V1514.

775. do. 975 min.x1324 max.x102   V754.

776. Rack & hook, swivel, wrought iron, 687, V758.

777. Rack & hook, for chimney crane, wrought iron, 330 max.x258 min.x72.

778. Hook for chimney crane, wrought iron, 170x21x50 V1579.

779. Rack & hook for chimney crane, wrought iron, 332 min.x 469 max.x50d. V1483.

HOOK EXTENSIONS

780. Wrought iron, 182x41x52 V1631. Donated by Mrs W. E. Fielden, and collected from a cottage at Poundsgate.

781. do. 156x66x41.

782. do. 315x61x55 V1630. prov. as no.267

783. do. 314x64x49 V1170.

784. do. 255x56x58 V1629. prov. as no.267.

KETTLE TILTERS OR IDLE-BACKS

785. Wrought iron,   369x354x42 V1168. Donated by Mrs W. E. Fielden, collected from Court Farm, Matencombe

786. do. 563x412x53 V1165. This, or 787/8, is from Moortown Farm, Gidleigh. Fielden.

787. do. 495x412 x53 V1169.

788. do. 648x181x42 V1168.

HAND HOOKS

789. Wrought iron, 148x104 V1176/1.

790. do. 138x101 V1176/2.

HANGERS: BALES

791. Wrought iron, hooks facing in opposite directions, 330x31 V1644. Donated by Mrs W. E. Fielden, collected from Hall Farm, Dartmoor.

792. do. hooks facing same direction, 390x48 V750/1.

793. do. hooks facing same direction, 405x35 V750/2.

BEARERS

794. Wrought iron, 583x442x339d. V1529.

795. do. 635x480x333 V1528.

CHIMNEY CRANES

796. Wrought iron, arms socketed into upright, diagonal brace fire welded to horizontal bar, 1180x770x63 V1543.

797. do, diagonal brace riveted to back of horizontal bar, 1053x938x24 V1595.

BRIGGS

798. Wrought iron, fire welded construction, 260x200x94 V696.

TRIVETS

799. Wrought iron, mainly half-round bar, 319x214d V1009.

800. do. joints socketed and riveted over, 355x320x214d V1008.

801. do. 275x254d. V1592.

802. do. 302x233d. V1593.

803. do. with firebar hooks, joints as no388, and fire welded hooks, 415x185x280 V791. Laycock collection.

804. do. wrought iron with brass top, joints as no.386, 350x169x310 V790.

805. do. cast brass with ebonised handle, stamped '9642'? on ring, 287x127x94 V798.

806. do. wrought iron, brass top, and ash? handle, 174x38x100, V1012

807. do. wrought iron frame riveted on to cast brass top, 323x151x200 V631.

STANDS

808. Cast brass top with turned brass legs, 214x65x111 V1459.

FIREBAR STANDS

809. Wrought iron, 313x283x158 V659.

810. do. Cast brass with hinged support and central porcelain plaque with gold banding 45x183d. V1704. Donated by Mrs A. F. Wane.

811. Brass, 307x134x184 V622. Laycock collection.

812. Cast brass with iron slide secured by a wing nut, 167x133x82 V1555.

813. With slide cast brass top marked '71' beneath, white glazed pottery handle mounted on a brass screw, 3016x128x146d. V1010.

814. Wrought iron, 360x201x121 V1011.

815. Iron, cast brass slide holding, by means of brass toggles, a sepia transfer-printed white earthenware tile embossed 'MINTON'S/CHINA WORKS/STOKE ON TRENT'. Ebonised turned handle on iron screw. 436x172x130 V1014. From a Chagford farm. Fielden.

816. do. wrought iron with cast brass slide and a turned oak handle, 422x146x128 V586.

817. do. wrought iron, 355x199x145 V601.

FOOTMEN

818. Wrought iron, riveted, 325x396x350.

819. do. 294x413x423 V663.

820. do. 319x440x369 V669.

821. do. 316x306x389 V792.

822. do. with brass plates, rods and rivets, 333x355x375 V1560. Fielden.

823. Iron frame, brass top and copper handles 350x523x325.

824. Cast brass with iron screw construction 300x290 triangular V661.

CATS

825. Mahogany, 298x310d. no.1200 V1521. Laycock 286.

826. do. 363x260 V1519. Laycock 65.

827. do. 358x280.

828. Beech, 245x320 V1524.

829. Brass, 400x350 no.2336 V1523.

830. do. 184x143 V1580.

TOASTERS

831. Toasting fork, wrought iron, 607x55 V765.

832. do. on brass shaft, 732x184 V764.

833. Hanging toaster, do. with knurled brass hand grip 473x114 V1454.

834. Down-hearth toaster, wrought iron, 121x266x175 V1464.

835. do., with drip tray, 101x380x202 V1463.

SALAMANDERS

836. Standing, wrought iron, 159x752x182 V1453.

837. do. stand missing, 990x120d. V612.

838. Ordinary, do. 649x102d. V610.

839. do. 726x123d. V620. Laycock 7.

SKEWERS

840. Wrought iron, 840x33 V1485.

SPITS

841. Hand-turned, wrought iron, 1136x88 V763. One of the 841-845 spits was collected from Middlecot Farm, Chagford, by Mrs Fielden.

842. do. 1120x100.

843. do. 1120x92 V751.

844. do. 1437x110 V762.

845. do. 1680x100 V533.

846. Pulley spit, wrought iron with beech pulley, 1313x196d.

847. do. pulley missing, but two dogs with heart terminals to their screws, 1678x127 V761.

848. do, iron pulley, 1222x210d. V773. Laycock.

849. Basket spit, wrought iron, 1195x194d.

850. Veruvolver spit, wrought iron, brass gear wheel and black wooden handle, 925x133d. V462.

851. do. basket spit, 945x317 V1450.

SPIT DOGS

852-53. Wrought iron, 795x265x525 V1511.

854-55. do. 597x358x285 with inverted heart-shaped plate on the fronts.

856-57. do. 617x313x550. Laycock.

858-59. do. 575x248x480 V619.

ROASTING JACKS

860. Weight-driven, iron and brass, with lead swans on the flywheel, the brass face engraved 'THO:/WILLS/ ST AUSTLE V1475.

861. do. iron and brass, the brass face plate being pierced for a plate engraved 'CON-STANTINE'. Round flywheel.

862. do. iron and brass, with diamond-shaped lead tips to the flywheel.

863. Jack winding handle, iron, 298 long V1063. Laycock.

864. do. 280 long V1792. Laycock.

865. Smoke jack, iron and brass, engraved 'W.M.CLA[RK?]/ EXETER' on the front bearing box 340/1936 no.1852. V1449. Donated by Major Gibbs, who collected it from the kitchen of his home at Pytte, Clyst St George, Topsham.

866. Bottle jack, iron, steel and brass in brass case, with 'GEO SALTER/ IMPROVED/WARRANTED' on the keyhole cover, and '40' and the Staffordshire knot on the base. 388x107 octagonal V1488.

867. do. 390x120 oct. no.1056 V1047. Collected Fielden, from a Torquay cottage.

868. do. '25 WARRANTED' on base, 395x106 oct.

869. do. with 'JOHN LINWOOD/WAR-RANTED' on embossed brass plate on front of body, and 'WARRANTED' stamped on the base. 383x103 oct. V1167.

870. As 868, but '10' on base 380x106 oct. V664.

871. Bottle jack flywheel, cast iron, black japanned surfaces, 61x170d. V1038.

872. do. no japanning. 50x155d. V1040.

873. do.70x195d. V1166.

874. do. slide hooks missing, 54x162d. V1039.

875. Bottle jack meat hook, iron, 338 (minimum)x25 V665.

876. Bottle jack bracket, steel, 87x165x40 no.2066.

877. do. brass, 82x243x64 V1177.

878. do. 118x243x132 no.2065.

879. do. 104x392x104 V1207.

880. Veruvolver jack, brass, bearing the embossed oval plate of 'PEARSE'S PATENT VERUVOLVER/ECONOMICAL ROASTING APPARATUS' and stamped 10486 on the front. 212x185d. V1471.

ROASTING SCREENS/HASTENERS

881. Standard tall, semi-circular folded and soldered tinplate screen, with mounting for bottle jack, door for basting, and a removable dripping pan with a hinge-lidded central dripping well (not illustrated) 1315x520 V665. Laycock.

DRIPPING PAN

882. Wrought iron, riveted, 300x300 +355 handle V665. Laycock 198.

BASTING LADLES

883. Sheet iron bowl riveted to wrought iron handle, 385x72d. V1376.

884. Brass(?) bowl fastened to wrought iron handle by copper rivets, 620x87d V1375.

885. Copper (originally plated?) with rat-tail back, 433x94x123 V1374.

886. Cast brass, 437x72 V1372.

887. do. 282x57 V1373.

888. do. 424x89 V1267.

889. as no. 887, 427x91 V1370.

890. Sheet brass, 467x93 V1260.

891. do. 408x82 V1265.

892. Sheet brass bowl riveted to wrought iron handle, 350x117 V1268.

BASTING MACHINE

893. Iron, steel and brass, 361 (at lowest setting) x130x60 (body).

GRID IRONS

894. Wrought iron, fire-welded, and inscribed 'PDM/ 1734' on handle, 98x608x342 V1494. Laycock 60.

895. do. through riveted, 110x535x271 64/1931 V788. Collected by Mrs Fielden from Broomhill, Ivybridge.

896. do. 122x474x276 V587.

897. do. 163x428x260 V565.

898. do. fire welded, 6x414x273 V585.

899. do. 85x553x251 V1456. Fielden.

900. do. riveted, 41x538x243 V599.

901. do. 6x570x95 V1172.

902. do. 5x431x76 V1171.

CHESTNUT ROASTERS

903. Stamped sheet iron with cast handles 'F&C', 486x216d. V1590.
904. Sheet brass, folded and pierced, 582x175d. V1468.

905. do. 582x168d. V1037

FRYING PANS

906. Down-hearth, copper, wired edge, riveted to wrought iron handle, 870x360d.

907. do. but with tapering handle, 1134x363d. V749.

908. do. oval, with tubular handle, pan 377x280. V749.

909. Frying pan, copper, tinned interior, wrought iron handle, pan 88x275d. V1148.

910. do. 102x178d. St Paul's Cross stamp on base, V1145.

911. do. cast iron with wrought handle riveted on, 694x331d. V784.

912. do. hanging, with 'No 9 J&J Siddons' cast into the base, 320x319d. V662.

913. do. plain base, 315x326d V732.

914. do. sheet iron, 230x248d. V1154. Fielden.

915. Sauté pan, construction and mark as 908, 135x285d. V1144.

BOILING VESSELS

916. Cauldron or crock, bell metal, 17th cent? 245x293 at rim, V1642 Collected by Mrs Fielden from a Chagford farm.

917. do. with the original hanging loops replaced by riveted iron plates, 145x170d. V1539. From Culmstock. Laycock.

918. do. round casting scar in centre of base, 126x197d.

919. Cast iron, with 'C-B-DALE/ 10 GALLS' cast into the side, for the Coalbrookdale foundry, Shropshire. 373x423.

920. do. no marks, 294x320d. V1663.

921. do. with a sheet iron lid having a riveted handle, 169x169 V829 & V 872.

922. do. with a copper lid having a sheet brass handle stamped 'BRENDON BROS/ CALLINGTON' ,Cornwall. 286x418.

923. do, oval, with sheet iron lid, with 'E.PUGH & CO/ 4 GALLS/ WEDNESBURY',

Staffordshire. 222x381x279 V1665.

924. do. with looped wrought iron bar suspension loops, and the base cast 'NO 3/Joseph & Jesse Siddons/Westbromwich/ 51/2 Galls'. 248x393x288 V1479.

925. do, circular, with eccentric circular projection in the base to fit into a ring on the top of a closed stove. 220x220d. V738.

926. Sheet brass, soldered circular panel in base, and side seam, then hand raised. The iron handle swings from riveted copper loops. 140x160d V1573.

927. Copper, hand raised, with wired edge, wrought iron handle and riveted loops, and a tinned interior, 200x250x210 V1133.

SKILLETS IN BELL-METAL AND BRASS

928. The handle is cast 'Ye WAGES OF SIN IS DEATH' followed by an arrow and 'F' probably for John Fathers, with descendants of the same name, who operated a foundry at Montacute near Yeovil c.1660s-c.1749 160x184d. V1572 Laycock.

929. The handle is engraved 'John Fry, E. Fry July 2 1748'. This skillet has fluted legs and a sheet brass patch fixed with copper rivets. 63x104d. V1571. Laycock.

930. The handle is cast 'T. P. B:WATER.I' for Thomas Pyke of Bridgewater, c.1750s-1800. 144x142d. V1155. Laycock 18.

931. The handle cast 'ROBT STREET & C;VI' for this Bridgewater founder of c.1760. 164x190 V1156. Laycock.

932. The handle cast as no.928, but is numbered 'V' 142x174d. V1570 Laycock.

933. The handle cast '2Q WARNER' for the Cripplegate Foundry in London, late 18th–early 19th cent. 154x188d. V118. Laycock.

934. The handle cast 'WASBROUGH*4' for William Wasborough and his descendants at 4, Narrow Wine Street, Bristol, c.1755-1848. 174x174d. V1565. Laycock.

935. Original handle replaced by one in wrought iron, riveted, 160x170d. V1157.

936. Original handle missing, and the stub ground off. 148x180d. V1547. Laycock.

SAUCEPANS/STEWPANS

937. Brass sheet, spun, with riveted sheet iron tubular handle, 90x175d. V1132.

938. Bellied stewpan with lid, seamed and raised copper sheet with wired edge, riveted tubular iron handle and tinned interiors 176x175d. V1134.

939. Cylindrical stewpan with lid, as no.936 but with a flat handle and an inset lid, three dots punched beneath the handle, 95x170d. V1127.

940. do. no lid, and with 'M' in dots punched beneath the handle, 95x175d. V1128.

941. do. 95x188d. V1125.

942. do. with folded base seam, 80x180d.

943. Cast iron, cast 'SWAIN/REGD/NO 3/ 2 PINTS' on base, tubular sheet iron handle and black enamelled sheet iron lid 98x130d V730.

944. do, cast 'T & C CLARK & CO/RD 455279/FIRST QUALITY/NO 3:2 PINTS' on base and '2/PINTS' on the side, fluted tubular sheet iron handle. 92x125d V1147.

945. do. but 'NO 5. 4 PINTS' and an embossed brass plate 'CLARK'S/4 PINTS/NO 5' on the handle of the sheet iron lid. 116x157d.

946. do. cast 'NO 4/J & J SIDDONS/WEST-BROMWICH/3 PINTS' on the base, and 'J & J SIDDONS WESTBROMWICH' on an embossed brass plaque on the sheet iron lid. Tubular sheet iron handle. 150x200d. 476/1965. Donated by Mrs Morris-Williams.

PIPKINS

947. Brown saltglazed stoneware, thrown handle, 95x109d. V1577. Laycock.

948. Light red earthenware, pulled handle, orange-brown lead glaze 79x96d. V1576. Fielden.

PRESERVING PANS

949. Cast and turned brass, with tubular and loop iron handles, riveted, 163x305d. V739. Donated by Mrs Groom.

950. Cast and turned brass 'maslin pan' with swing bow iron handle, 138x277d. V1137.

951. do., fixed bow handle, riveted, 177x340d. V1476.

952. Spun sheet brass, wired edge, and fixed bow handle, riveted, 138x312d. V733.

953. Cast and turned brass, with riveted cast brass handles, 99x439d. V831.

954. Hand-raised untinned copper, wired edge and riveted cast brass handles, 105x332d. V1628.

SUGAR BOILER

955. Untinned raised copper, with turned oak handle, 119x225d. V1148.

FISH KETTLE

956. untinned copper, both soldered and folded seams, and replaced riveted handles, 153x475x310 71/1931 V1487. Fielden.

SKIMMERS

957. Copper, with soldered joints, 640x110 V1272.

958. Sheet brass bowl riveted to wrought iron handle, 624x185d. V1381.

959. do. 734x128d. V1380. Laycock 12.

960. do. 742x199d. V1300. Laycock 85.

961. do. 672x215d. V1276. Laycock 17.

962. do. 669x123d. V1274.

963. do. 624x195d. V1275.

964. do 663x185d. V1273.

PASTRY JIGGER

965. Cast brass, 125x25d. no.1146 V1361. Purchased.

OVEN DOORS

966. Buff earthenware with heavy gritted fabric 320x380 V743. Laycock 196.

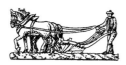

967. do., with '4' scratched into the top, indicating the size of the oven, 350x305 V743. Laycock 196.

FAGGOT FORKS

968. Wrought iron, with hollow tubular handle, 1185x84 V779.

969. Wrought iron, 1163x90 V772.

970. do. 1114x84 V1304.

PEELS

971. Wrought iron on wooden handle.

972. Wrought iron, 1550x219.

BAKING IRONS

973. Cast iron, worn thin across the front edge, 8x400d V658.

974. do. 11x380d. V657.

975. do. 9x400d. V656.

BAKERS

976. Cast iron, 104x302d. V1661.

977. do. 162x257d V1660.

978. do. 140x270d. V1585.

979. do, cast 'CARRON/15 GALLS' on body and 'CARRON' on lid, with '15' on the removable bottom plate which rests inside. 235x378d. V1463. Purchased by Mrs Fielden from R. Kernick, blacksmith, Widecombe-in-the-Moor, on 1 November 1933.

WAFER TONGS

980. Wrought iron, with flowers and a star engraved on the plates, 845x125d.
981. do. with Prince of Wales Feathers and Garter star, 837x128d. 454/1964 V611. Donated by Mrs F. G. Callard.

BREAD SCALES

982. Wrought iron, polished, 415x228 nos 2329 and 509. Laycock. These were described in 1936 as being 'recently used in the Minehead district'.

GINGERBREAD MOULDS

Most of this group probably dates to 1825-30, since *Paul Pry*, a comedy by John Poole, was first staged in 1825, and, although the inaccurate royal arms, the initials 'GR' on both the arms and the horse, and the figure of the crowned king on horseback may be earlier, they were certainly carved before the death of George IV in 1830. They were all found in the long-disused oven of a cottage bakery at Bovey Tracey. no.3576. Donated by Miss E. Tracey of Bovey Tracey, 1951.

983. Royal arms and supporters, V641.

984. King George on horseback, and a man holding a horse by its bridle, V639.

985. Paul Pry, and a figure in a bicorn hat, V1369.

986. W. Corder, and a small horse, V640.

987. Sailor, and a man on a horse, V634.

988. Fiddler, and a large horse with 'GR' on the saddlecloth, V638.

989. Man in fairman's chicken suit, and an elephant, V633.

990. A man and woman, arm-in-arm, and a vase of flowers, V643.

991. The dog 'CLEANLY' licking a cauldron, and a windmill, V642.

992. A sheep, and a cannon, V635.

993. Two square panels, one with an acorn, the other with a beehive.

DRINK PREPARATION

994. Beer skimmer, copper sheet, wire-edged and soldered to a tubular copper haft, into which the wooden handle is secured by an iron nail. 285x1170 407/1937. no.2120 Laycock.

995. Screw spiggot, sycamore? with asH screw 285x73x54 V569/2 no.1568. unprovenanced.

996. Tap spiggot, elm with boxwood? tap 212x135x46 V1349.

WINE BOTTLES

997. Light green glass, 125x100d. no.3904. Miss Jean Holland, Bishopsteignton.

998. Green glass, with seal 'Bodley/Spelligue/1723' 165x161d V1428.

999. Dark green glass, with seal 'Cha/Pugh/1763' and engraved signature 'John Pugh/1794' on shoulder 280x91d V1430.

1000. As 999 280x91d V1429/1.

1001. As 999, but with seal 'I/Dally E[sq.]/Thorvertn/1770' 280x98d V1420.

1002. Dark green glass, with seal 'John Pugh/1794' 267x93d V1429/2.

1003. do. 'E. Browne/Blakemore/1804' 244x114d V1433. Donated by Messrs Ash.

1004. do. Carew crest and 'H. C.' 268x88d. V1432/1 42/1952 no.3646 Donated By Miss T. Brown.

1005. As 1004 264x90d V1432/2.

1006. Dark green glass, 285x107d V1431. Donated by Miss Ash.

1007. Green glass, 285x107d V1431 Donated by Miss Ash.

1008. As 1007 but with double ring round neck 298x94 V1427. Donated by Miss Ash.

1009. Light green glass, 268x110d V1438. Laycock. This hung on the wall of his 'Den', and might be a salad-oil bottle which, inverted into a glass jar of water, acted as a barometer.

1010. Brown hock bottle, moulded, with no pontil mark, 348x76d. Donated by Mr G. Downe.

1011. As 1010 343x72d.

1012. Light green glass, mould blown with 18-petal rosette in base and '...NDS/PATENT' cast into the stopper. The metal clips are stamped 'RYLANDS/PATENT/PULL' 275x 159d V1439 no.2243. Found at Torre. Donated by Mr Stephens.

BOTTLING EQUIPMENT

1013. Pewter, 183xc.127d V1228 292/1963. Donated H. Unsworth.

1014. do. tube broken off short 104x110d V1227.

1015. Bottling 'boot', thick black leather, stitched, 206x109d V1420.

1016. Cork press, oak with iron hinge, 77x305x50 390/1936. Laycock.

CIDER

1017. Scoop for crushed apples, oak, nailed, 119x332x122 V813.

1018. Dipper, oak, coopered, 351x165x135 base V1323. Laycock.

1019. Dipper, oak, nailed, 350x198x170 base. Laycock.

COFFEE

1020. Roaster, sheet iron with brass-cased clockwork motor bearing an embossed plate 'SAVAGE/LONDON' and the Royal Arms, all mounted on iron firebar hooks 268x258x380. Laycock.

1021. Roaster, pressed copper ball rotating on brackets cast '1/2 lb' over a copper bowl mounted on a copper base. Base 146x156d V1583 no.2448 no.575. Donated by Miss Aynger.

1022. Mill, turned *lignum vitae* with steel mechanism, the hinged handle extension missing but replaced with a brass knob 148x99d base V965.

1023. do. lid missing 154x104d base V1345. Laycock 228.

1024. Mill, oak with brass hopper and feet, with steel fittings 224x172sq V1584/1 517/1938 no2359. Laycock.

1025. Mill, cast iron, black lacquered, and spun brass hopper. The top bears the inscription 'Bruertons Patent I & C Clark & Co Manufacturers' and an embossed brass plate to the adjustment screw 'I & C CLARK & CO. WOLVERHAMPTON' 149x165sq V1733.

1026. Mill, similar to 1025 but with ornate cast decoration to the handle, top and base moulding, and an embossed brass plate 'I & C CLARK'S IMPROVED COFFEE MILL' with the Royal Arms. The base is cast 'Registered Feb 17, 1842 No.1100 I & C Clark No.3' 135x145sq V967/1.

1027. French mill, walnut with lacquered brass and iron fittings, the mill being turned by a vertically-rotating handle and crown gears. An oval embossed plate reads 'PEUGEOT FRERES/VALENTIGNEY (DOUBS)' with a lion standing on an arrow as trademark 240x125x158 V966/1. Laycock 66.

LIQUID HEATING

1028. Fountain, cast iron with brass tap and knob to lid, and a forged bail handle. Base cast 'KENDRICK & SONS/ 4 Galls' 280d V1641. Laycock 256?

1029. do., but with suspension loop instead of a hook. Base cast '2 GALLS' with an L in a diamond as trademark. 240x 235d V1477. Laycock 257?

1030. do., but with forged handles to sides of shoulder. Base cast 'I & C CLARK & CO LTD/ENGLAND/BEST QUALITY/3 GALLS' 273x275d V1478.

1031. Dartmoor kettle, copper body with dovetail seam round base and down back, seamed and raised spout, brass hinge plates and cast brass bail handle. Cylindrical handle to lid. 192x185d base V1541.

1032. do. 183x174 V1130.

1033. do. 168x173d V1589.

1034. do.but with turned brass knob, 193x194 V1160. Laycock 253.

1035. do. and also wrought iron handle 220x190 V1161. Laycock 35.

1036. Copper kettle, dovetail seam down back, raised, re-bottomed, cast brass handl and knob to lid 315x205d V734.

1037. Copper kettle, dovetail seam down back, raised, tubular handle on cast brass supports, and brass rim to opening. The lid is a replacement. 209x128x100 V1035.

1038. Cast iron kettle, white enamel interior, lid marked 'No O', shoulder 'T. SHELDON & CO /NO *O' and base '3 PINTS' 225x148d V1159.

1039. Cast iron kettle, similar to 1038, but with oval panel 'T.SHELDON & CO/No *3' on shoulder and 'T.SHELTON & CO LTD WOLVERHAMPTON/NO 3/3PINTS/ENGLAND' on base 281x183d V1540.

WHITE ALE HEATERS

1040. Tinplate, conical with folded seam, wire edge and wrought iron handle 348x153d V985. Probably 726/1965 from Kingsteignton, donated by E. A. J. Elliot.

1041. do. 340x133 V984.

1042. Copper, conical with dovetail seam, wire edge and wrought iron handle 373x175d V983.

1043. do. with tubular copper handle 120d V1383. Laycock 260.

1044. do. with strap handle and replaced tip 102d. V1382.

1045. Copper, slipper shape, folded seams, soldered, tinned interior, and brass knob, c.250x90d V1387. Donated by Mr A. H. Ogilvie.

1046. do. with iron handle and hinged lid c.415x79d V827.

1047. do. with tubular copper handle, hinged lid missing, engraved 'A.Davis/ 1771' c.125x117d V1396. Laycock 245.

FOOD SERVING VESSELS

1048. Dish, pewter, with hammered bouge, punched 'GW/MT/1767' on rim 378d V1248. Fielden.

1049. Similar to 1048, but with pewterer's marks on base (recorded as no6039 in Cotterell as being recorded on a piece dated 1796) 375d V1311 no2993. Donated by T. Edwards.

1050-51. Egg cups, pewter, 57x46d V1261/1-2. Laycock.

1052. Egg cup, turned wood, 62x42d V1022. Laycock 38.

1053. Pepper caster, pewter, 124x56d V1273.

1054. do. 138x61d V1240.

1055. do. 110x49d. V1239.

1056-57. do. 100x46d. Holes punched as 5-pointed stars, and base stamped 'JAMES DIXON/& SONS/51 V1235/1-2. Laycock 26.

1058. do. 124x43d marked as 1056-57, but '52'. Laycock 26.

1059. do. 115x52d V1238.

1060. do. cast and spun brass 154x62d V836.

1061. Salt cellar, pewter with blue-glazed white pottery liner 52x71d V1263/1. Donated by E. H. Moore.

1062. pair to 1061, 57x77d V1263/2 no2708.
1063. Salt mill, turned wood, polished, 82x39d V1344.

1064. Mustard pot, pewter with blue glass liner, 70x57d V1220.

1065. do. liner missing, 70x58d V1225.

EATING UTENSILS: TRENCHERS

1066. Elm? with knife cuts and wear on both faces, 196x205x22 V1359. Laycock.

1067. Turned wood 18x88d V839.

1068. Walnut?,turned, 23x68d V1199. Fielden.

1069. Sycamore 18x227d V1069.

1070. do. 20x234d.

PEWTER PLATES

1071. Reeded rim, marked, and with a faint Tudor rose within an oval stamped on the back, 236d V1246. Laycock 49.

1072. Plain rim, marked beneath rim for Thomas Page of Bristol, who obtained his freedom from the Pewterer's Company on 10 October, 1737, and with an engraved 'GM' cartouche on the rim. 16x238d. Laycock 45.

1073. Plain rim, stamped 'TL', and a mark on the back 14x234d V1247/1.

1074. do. 14x234d V1247/2.

1075. Plain rim, marked on back, 15x241d.

1076. Plain narrow rim marked on the back (marks recorded in Cotterell as no6039 occurring on a piece dated 1796) 10x227d V1243. Laycock 47.

1077. Concave rim, mark on the back 'ALDERSON/BLENHEIM STREET/LONDON' 20x245d V1242. Laycock 46.

1078. do. 20x245. Laycock 248.

1079. Concave rim, back marked three times with a triangle of the initials !/K/S/W. On the face is a wriggle-work picture with the inscription: 'Das neue Ekebour folleben und alle Hockzeit Gefted a neben' 22x222 V1245 L44.

CUTLERY

1080. Steel dinner knife, bone handle 268l V1667.

1081. As 1079 222l V167.

1082. do. stamped 'TAYLORS CELEBRAT-ED/[eye]/WITNESS/SHEFFIELD' on blade, riveted bone scales 239l V1667.

1084. As 1081 240l V1667.

1085-6. do. blades stamped 'TRYMILLS/ FRANK MILLS & Co/ SHEFFIELD', synthetic ivory handles 209l V1667.

1087-1104. Set of 9 buffalo-horn handled steel knives and forks. The knives are stamped 'W.M.MITCHELL & Co/MARKET STREET/MANCHESTER' 208l, the forks 164l 476/1965. Donated Mrs D. Morris-Williams.

1105. Fork, steel, with wooden? handle 222l V1667.

1106. do. with riveted buffalo-horn scales 192l V1667.

1107-8. Knife and fork, steel, with brass ferrules stamped '10', the handles being of stag horn, the integral section of the skull being carved in the form of the head of an elderly man wearing a large felt hat. Knife

230l. Fork 205l. 38/1935 no749 carved by French prisoners of war at Princetown. Fielden.

1109. Spoon, horn, pressed, 237x56 V1367. Laycock.

1110. do. with whistle in end of handle 166x35 V1336. Laycock.

1111. Apple scoop, made from sheep shinbone, turned back, front incised 'J. C.' with inlaid horn? heart and diamond design. 135x30 V1365 no2607. Donated by Mrs Mitchell.

1112. do. front incised with an X 122x30 V999.

1113. do. turned back 125x26 V1364 no. 2608. Donated by Mrs Mitchell.

DRINK SERVING: LEATHER JUGS

1114. Stitched, with handle formed integrally with the body, 410x159d V1424. Laycock.

1115. do. with rivets through handle, and incised with a crown and 'C R 1646' (reproduction) 417x198d V1423. Laycock.

1116. do. 347x164d V1419. Laycock.

1117. do, punched with four diamond-shaped panels of 3x3 dots, and the indistinct initials IW 264x132d V1421. Laycock.

1118. Toby jug, wooden peg and stitched construction, with remains of red-painted cheeks, black outlined eyes, etc. 405x219x 190 V3180. According to the accessions register, this and nos 1117-19 were 'probably made in a factory at Sargadalos in Galicia. This factory closed down about 1750. Owned by an Englishman, it made a kind of pottery toby jug [in leather] which was exported to England. Property of Mr Ault of Torquay, from whom they were purchased by Mr Middlewich for £100 and given to Mr Rotherham. Donated by C. E. Rotherham, 1947'. Similar, much larger figures of Elizabeth I and Charles I from a York public house, are now in the York Castle Museum.

1119. do. 295x177x150 V3181.

1120. do. 289x208x160 V3182.

1121. do. 253x172x145 V3183.

LEATHER BOTTLES

1122. Stitched, incised 'RW' 94x78 V1409.

1123. do. incised 'IM' on one side and punched 'RW'? and rosette stamps on the other 115x110 V1410.

1124. do. burnt 'TR' with horn brand on base and each shoulder 176x159 V1415.

1125. Round flask with two pressed sides stitched together through a U-section strip 665x175d V1411. Laycock 29.

1126. Half-round flask, stamped '3' in dots on the base, with a metal cap with hasp and padlock 334x118x70.

POTTERY JUGS

1127. Light red earthenware, pale brown glaze dipped down to shoulder, thumb-print at base joint of handle. 235x165d. V1653 205/1934 West country. Miss B. Chase?

1128. Light red earthenware, with stacking stains on base, with rich orange/brown lead glazed interior and rim 364x175d V647 369/1936 no1969. Mrs Groom per C. H. Laycock.

1129. Brown salt-glazed stoneware 306x134d V1444, Fielden,

1130. Owl or pill, buff earthenware with light yellow glaze on neck and shoulders 190x127d V1441. Made at the Verwood potteries and used in Dorset. Fielden.

1131. Creamware, coloured enamel decoration including flail, shears and harrow, pitchfork, rake and scythe, a sheaf of corn, a sickle, a plough, and a fork and spade 151x95d C779. Late 18th cent. probably Leeds Pottery.

1132. do. with harrow, spade, crossed scythe and pitchfork, a sheaf of corn, a sickle, a crossed flail and rake, a plough an axe and a fork 125x75d C780. Laycock.

1133. do. with dung fork, crossed spade and fork, a plough, a harrow, a crossed sickle and pitchfork, a sheaf of corn, a scythe and flail, and a rake 162x94 C778. Laycock.

1134. White, clear glazed earthenware, pink lustre decoration and black transfer prints, including a ploughing scene:

> *'He that by the plough would thrive himself must either hold or drive'*

a farming scene:

> *'Industry produceth wealth'*

and on the other side:

> *'Let the wealthy and great*
> *Roll in splendour and state,*
> *I envy them not I declare it.*
> *I eat my own lamb,*
> *My own chickens and ham,*
> *I shear my own fleece and I wear it.*
> *I have lawns, I have bowers,*
> *I have fruits I have flowers,*
> *The lark is my morning alarmer,*
> *So jolly boys now,*
> *Here's God speed the plough,*
> *Long life and success to the farmer.'*

106x130d C284. Laycock. Sunderland, early 19th cent.

1135. do. with the above verse surmounted by 'In God is all our trust', with 'Industry produceth wealth' below, and on the other side agricultural devices and 'Trust in God the husbandmans diligence provides bread' 150x86d C310. Laycock.

1136. do. on one side 'God speed the plough' and 'The Farmer's Creed':

> *'Let this be held the farmer's creed.*
> *For stock seek out the choicest breed,*
> *In peace and plenty let them feed.*
> *Your land sow with the best of seed,*
> *Let it not dung or dressing need.*
> *Inclose and drain it with all speed,*
> *And you will soon be rich indeed'*

On the other side, agricultural motifs and 'He that by the plough would thrive himself must either hold or drive' and 'Industry produceth wealth' 150x93d C307. Laycock.

FIRKINS

1137. Oak, with four riveted iron hoops, leather thong slotted and pegged through the bung-block, and the bung secured on a cord. Branded 'TR' on one end. 218x125 V1348.

1138. do. thong and bung missing 245x158 V1645.

1139. do. branded 'TP' and inscribed 'JM' on both ends 201x120 V1328.

1140. do. bung block missing 215x117 V1327.

1141. do. triangular section, branded 'TV' on one end 275x180x170 V1448.

1142. do. 235x135x103 V1329.

1143. Oak, oval section, glass ends, hazel? bands, brass screw stopper 280x125x101 V814. Laycock.

CIDER DIPPERS

1144. Copper, cylindrical, seamed and wire edge, wrought iron handle129x124d V1617.

1145. do. dovetail jointed, soldered and raised, tinned all over, engraved with earl's coronet and the initials 'HG', wrought iron handle. A late 19th cent. bain-marie pot used as a dipper 107x90d V858.

1146. Copper, dovetail joint, raised, wire edge, turned wood handle painted black 96x107d V1131.

1147. do. tubular iron handle 108x120d. V1388.

1148. do. turned wood handle 66x75d V1384.

1149. Copper, dovetail joint and folded seam, wire edge, wrought iron handle. Probably originally used for making Turkish coffee 63x58d V1385.

COFFEE POT

1150. Copper, folded seams, wired edge, tinned interior, brass knob and turned mahogany? handle 220x120d V826.

TEA WARES

1151. Britannia metal? with ebonised handle, base stamped 'I/DIXON & SON' 80x98d V1224.

1152. do. inscription erased, stamped '4/ SHEFFIELD/SILVER PLATED/15' 175x145d.

1153. do. stamped '8' 195x300l V1231. Laycock 64.

1154. do. 152x155d V1250.

1155. do. stamped 'WARRANTED BEST METAL 885' and '4/VR/RICHARD HARRIS/& SONS/SHEFFIELD/127' 164x c150d V1232. Laycock 68.

1156. do. hot water jug, plaited cane insulation to handle 177x70d V1223. Laycock 27.

1157. do. cream jug 85x56d A219.

PUNCH WARES

1158. Punch bowl, brown salt-glazed stoneware, Derbyshire?,inscribed 'John Hall and Rebeckah his wife 1740' 160x301d. Found, broken, in a cellar in St Marychurch Road, Torquay. Donated Mr & Mrs Newton.

1159. Ladle, turned sycamore with carved handle 186x42d V855. Laycock 41.

1160. do. turned handle screwed into turned bowl 290x56d no2036. Donated K. M. Law.

1161. do. 318x62d V850.

1162. Turned mahogany handle socketed into haft of pewter bowl 328x58d V1350.

1163. Dark-stained wood handle with tapering screw haft into pewter bowl 307x94w V1371.

1164. Horn handle riveted on to turned horn bowl 269x c86d 893/1947 no3186. Donated C. E. Rotherham.

DRINKING VESSELS: TANKARDS
LEATHER

1165. Cylindrical, applied handle, with three bands and a row of ring and dot punch marks around the rim 178x104d V1413.

1166. do. with integral handle, with rows of concentric circle, indented semi-circle, and ring and dot punched around the rim, incised bands around the body, three bands and ring punching around the handle, base, and deep incised band 57x190l V1412.

1167. do. with integral handle 132x135l V1408.

1168. do. 205x163l.

1169. Cylindrical with strap handle and brass? strip riveted around the rim V1414

PEWTER

1170. Marked 'JAMES YATES','QUART' and 'VR' for James Yates of Birmingham c.1800-1840 165x110d V1210.

1171. Marked 'GR','WR','QUART' and 'DERBY' stamps 150x120d V1249 no.2894 from Church Inn, Torbryan. R.H.Ogilvie.

1172. Identical to 1163, but with 'JAMES YATES','QUART' and 'EXON' (for Exeter) stamps 152x124d V1209. Laycock 19.

1173. Marked 'JAMES YATES','1/2 PINT' and 'VR', and engraved 'D. Harvey' round the body. 94x82d V1214 no.2896 A. H. Millward.

1174. Marked 'VR','PINT' and 'WR EXON' 110x101d V1242 no.2895 prov. as 1171.

WOODEN

1175. Oak, with carved handle and four riveted iron bands 183x97d V1331.

HORN MUGS

1176. Engraved with fox-hunting scene 98x48d V1399.

1177. Plain, 127x54 V339. Laycock 51.

1178. do. incised 'W' on base 107x55d V1404.

1179. do. 94x66d V1406. Laycock 37A.

1180. do. 93x66d V1400. Laycock 37B.

1181. do. 105x47d. V1397.

1182. do. pairs of holes drilled through opposite sides of the rim 79x45d V1401.

EARTHENWARE MUGS

1183. White earthenware with clear glaze, black transfer printed decoration overpainted with bright enamel colours. It

shows the Farmers' Arms of agricultural implements set within a shield, flanked by a maid with a rake on the left and a man with a scythe on the right, and beneath, the motto 'God speed the plough' 120x91d C601. Laycock.

1184. do. two-handled. One side shows agricultural implements and a scroll 'Trust in God. The Husbandman's dilligence provides bread', the other has the verse 'Let the wealthy and great...' (*see no.1132*) within a border of agricultural implements. 96x106d C602. Laycock.

1185. do. with farming motifs and 'God speed the plough' on one side, and on the other the verse 'Let the wealthy and great...' (*see no.1132*) flanked by sheaves of corn and above a scroll 'Industry produceth wealth'. Base marked '/1' in red 102x97d. C603. Laycock.

1186. do. black transfer on base '[F]armers arms: B&L' 102x109d C604. Laycock.

1187. do. 'Let the wealthy and great...' (*see no.1132*) in border of scrolls and agricultural implements on one side, and again, in sections, on the other, along with 'The Farmers Arms', 'In God is our trust', and 'He that by the plough would thrive/Himself must either/Hold or drive/God speed the plough' base marked with a black '+' and a dot 132x138d C605. Laycock.

TOBACCO, BOXES

1188. Lead, cast and soldered, 170x152x107.

1189. do. 120x93x96 V1254.

1190. Pewter, cast and spun, with deep-flanged inner lid, fine engraving on all external surfaces, and chinese characters impressed into the base 148x119d V1222. Laycock 67.

1191. Lead, cast and soldered, with identical hunting scenes in relief on each side, and a peacock knob 115x95sq V1251.

1192. Pewter sheet, soldered, 30x194x78. Laycock.

1193. Horn, pressed, 30x108x92 806 no2356. Laycock.

PIPE

1194. Iron churchwarden 520x20d. Laycock.

PIPE STOPPERS

1195. Greyhound and rabbit carved in boxwood 81x11d V244.

1196. Hand and pipe, cast brass 46x13d V243.

1197. Booted leg, cast brass, with 'WK' monogram engraved on end 48x10d.

PIPE KILNS

1198. Wrought iron, riveted 178x340 V1499. Laycock 58.

1199. do. riveted and fire welded 219x399 V1500. Laycock 59.

1200. do. riveted 230x345 V1501.

1201. do. riveted and fire welded 196x370 V1582.

SNUFF BOXES

1202. Walnut? boot with sliding lid and copper lace-holes 89x144 V3894 no2975 'probably made in the Torquay area around 1850'. Donated W. H. V. Walters.

1203. Oak, engraved floral sprays, with brass hinge, copper-nailed soles and lead heel-plates 47x81 V3845 no2908. Donated A. H. Millward.

GAMES

1204-5. Cockspurs, steel (56l) on leather straps (73x25 and 85x27) V1073/1&2 no755a&b 672/1900 from Kingsbridge near Marlborough. Donated W. R. Beer.

1206-11. Bowls, hardwood, painted black, white, red, yellow, blue and green respectively, each being stamped 'T.C.C./B.S.' c.140d. 564/1895 Padget Blake collection. These bowls, reputedly those used by Sir Francis Drake for his game on Plymouth Hoe before departing to defeat the Armada, were formerly displayed at Trematon Castle, Cornwall (see Torquay Directory 17th April,1895) but are 19th century in date.

1212. Domino box, pine carcase, with watercolour panels of (prison?) buildings along each side, flower baskets at the ends, and two ladies and two gentlemen on the lid, all glazed and mounted in carved bone plates. The box holds 29 dominos. 49x70x167 314/1935 no1601. Made by French prisoners of war at Princetown c.1813. Laycock.

1213. do. with an additional prison scene on each side, man and woman on top, and animal scenes on both ends 89x102x252 755/1943 no2962. Donated by Mrs H. Lane.

1214. Dominos, set of 37, bone, black numbers and red cross-line 24x15x4 V3656 identical to those made by the prisoners of war at Princetown. Donated Misses Russell.

1215. Domino made of slate by prisoners of war at Princetown c.1814, a blank five, 36x18x3 739a 1008/1928. Donated F. W. Askham.

1216. do. a five, 19x20x2 739b.

1217. Card box, pine carcase covered with flat stips of coloured straw arranged in geometric patterns 113x53 552/1899. Donated Dr Karkeek.

Wool Preparation

1218. Woolcomb, four layers of cast steel prongs set in horn on an ash handle with iron-rimmed holes for fixing to the pad-post. The head is stamped 'JOHN WHALLEY/CAST STEEL/KEIGHLEY/1844' 335x195w V1492. From the Barnstable woollen industry. Fielden.

Spinning

1219. Spinning wheel, walnut?, stamped on the back edge of the base board 'TUER-LINCKX' 'PUTTE' baseboard 31x175x40 wheel 378d.

1220. Spinning wheel, oak and pine, black stained, base board 172x327x36 wheel 385d.

1221. Spinning wheel, walnut?, base board 61x160x25 wheel 395d V1515.

1222. Spinning wheel, oak with brown stain, 990h wheel 470d V374 flax wheel

from Cumbria Donated Mrs Morris-Williams December 1984.

1223. Spinning wheel, dark-stained timbers with applied pewter decoration. There is a screw-tension device for the single-groove wheelband, the flyer being braked by a leather friction band adjusted by an encircling cord tightened by turning an adjacent peg. 745h wheel 390d. Laycock 92. This wheel comes from Switzerland, cf. D. Baud-Bovy *Peasant Art in Switzerland* (London 1924) pl.281 and P. Baines *Spinning Wheels, Spinners & Spinning* (London 1977) 141.

1224. Girdle or belt spinning wheel, mahogany, with brass and iron mechanism. Popular in fashionable circles in the late 18th century, both in England and the continent, the leading English makers were the Webster family, clockmakers in Shrewsbury. See P. Baines (ref above) 163.

1225. Clock or wrap wheel. Oak, pine etc. with black stain, the hub having a screw thread which operates gearing on the column, to give a click when a pre-determined length of yarn has been wound on to the wheel from the bobbins removed from the spinning wheels. 820hx770d V1495

1226. Doubling or plying wheel, oak etc., with brass and iron fittings. baseboard 484x154x30 wheel 342d. A holder for two bobbins supplies single-ply yarn to two arms of a flyer, which twists the yarns together before they are gathered on a bobbin mounted on the vertical spindle V496 **1227.** Bobbin or pirn winder, oak, base 470x140x37 wheel 285d V1493.

1228. do. pine, oak etc. with brown varnish, inscribed in ink 'L M TREGALE 1930' on base. Base 447x130x50 wheel 165d V1494.

1229. do. mahogany and oak base, polished, base 195x110x52 wheel 175d V1491.

Knitting Sheaths

1230. Dark polished wood with brass ferrule 194x13x15 V1027.

1231. Turned wood, double-ended, 177x15d V1023 probably from South Wales.

1232. Mahogany? carved with heart, diamond and other motifs, and inscribed

'Forget me not' 198x20x15 V1106. Stylistically from Weardale, Co. Durham.

1233. Mahogany, with ball-cage, chain, diagonal cow-band slot, inlaid hearts and incised decoration, including 'M+Bell'. Stick 183x22x22 V1074. Stylistically from Upper Teesdale, County Durham.

1234. Wood, square shaft, with diagonal square knob and two tiers of hearts and 'M.A.R.', dovetail section cow-band slot 161x15x15 V2144 no414. Donated Mrs King.

NETTING NEEDLE

1235. Mahogany? 205x18x2 V1075.

SAMPLER FRAME

1236. Mahogany, with brass turnscrews and ratchet mechanisms for the rollers, linen tapes nailed down sides, and pieces of unfinished wool-work samplers on the rollers. Base 417x153x18 V1611 262/1962 no3977. Donated Mrs T. R. A. Windeatt.

WORKBOX

1237. Pine carcase covered in bone plates, engraved with formalised foliage borders, or pierced to reveal a layer of gold-coloured foil beneath. The paper-lined interior bears a label inscribed: This is a carved walrus ivory casket, 19th cent. from Archangel, Russia. See C. Holme (ed.) *Peasant Art in Russia* (London 1912) figs. 171-2. 102x 224x142.

SAVINGS: MONEY BOXES

1238. Light red earthenware, white slip dip, yellow lead glaze with streaks of dark brown iron/manganese staining 166x60d C823. Yorkshire, probably Burton-in-Lonsdale, although similar glazes are seen on wares from Castleford in the Yorkshire Museum collection.

1239. Red Wealden earthenware, iron flecked, glazed to a rich orange-brown under a lead glaze 81x54d C826. Probably Sussex pottery.

1240. Buff salt-glazed stoneware with iron dipped top, inscribed in ink on base 'J.D.St Neots 1935' 175x70d V1069 no2271. Laycock.

1241. Buff earthenware fowl, press-moulded, iron-dipped basket, and lead glazed 85x88x59 C827 no 2771.

1242. Buff stoneware chest of drawers, moulded, with iron or manganese brown glaze. Slot in back 80x74x46 C824 561/1939 no2441. Laycock.

1243. Materials as 1242. Hexagonal gothic cottage 100x84x58 C825 no2440. Laycock.

1244. Mahogany, French polished, slot in base 70x76 hexagonal V1201. Fielden.

1245. Cast iron, polychrome painted decoration. The door opens to reveal a 'CASHIER' with a tray, who, on pressing a button on the side, closes the door and throws the coin inside. Cast in the base: 'Patd/AUG 5 1873/MAR 7 1876 126x121 x100. Laycock 34.

AGRICULTURE: TRANSPORT
OXEN

1246. Yoke, elm? with iron fittings 1250x138 633/1897. From Hartland. Donated M.Cole.

1247-50 Cues, wrought iron, 359/1936. Found at Torbryan in 1923. Donated by W. W. G. Maunder.

HORSES

1251. Horse shoe, wrought iron, 117x V1057/1. Found near North Bovey. Donated by John Hill.

1252. do. 120x123 V1057/2 320/1880. Found in an old house at Newton Abbot in 1879. Donated by John Prowse.

1253. do. 127x127 provenance as 1252.

1254. do 138x135 V9051 no751. Found at Torbryan Farm 1932.

1255. do. 98x126 V1052 no751. Provenance as 1254.

1256-7. do, with india rubber inserts in the face, and spiked clips on the back, for surgical use 128x114 no1543.

1258. Turf shoe, leather, rivetted, 164x154 V1797. Donated Mr B. Sessions.

PACK HORSES

1259. Pack saddle, wood frame with straw-filled canvas pad and iron fittings. 625x770 V1722 592/1895. From Exmoor Donated Dr Karkeek.

1260. do. 550x630x760 V721. Provenance as 1259.

1261. Dung pot, probably oak and ash, 665x440x360. Provenance as 1259.

1262. do. 710x427x345. Provenance as 1259.

1263. do. provenance as 1259.

1264. do. provenance as 1259.

1265. Crooks, wood, 855x648 V571/2. Provenance as 1259.

1266. do. 980x645 V571/1 613/1896. Provenance as 1259.

1267. Crubs, pine, 430x500.

1268. do. 430x510.

DRAUGHT HORSES

1269. Team bells, four brass bells fitted to a wooden board, with a leather canopy fitted with brass-headed nails, four oval brasses and iron brackets 546x334x180 V520. Laycock.

1270. do. five mounted on a wooden bar sheathed in embossed leather decorated with late Victorian reclining lady, foliage etc. and fitted on pierced wrought iron brackets 603x74x227 V1481. Laycock 249.

1271. Reins, leather, 24wide, with iron buckles at each end, 540/1968. From a farm near Widecombe. Donated by L. A. J. Jackman.

1272. Nosebag, woven fibre, webbing and leather straps, nailed to an oval wooden baseboard 46x45x25. From a farm near Widecombe V1723 540/1968. Donated by L. A. J. Jackman.

1273. Bit, wrought iron, bit 175l. Dug up at Ilsham in 1952 V1068 no3644. Donated by Miss Webb.

1274. Hames, each stamped 'SOLID BRASS NO 2' and 'PATENT DOUBLE CASED' with a carthorse in an oval panel on each heart-shaped plate, and with steel and leather fittings 825l V456.

1275. Bargham, (the flat piece of leather fitting on top of the horse collar) leather, stitched, and decorated with brasses 460x328 V1043.

HORSE BRASSES

1276. Cast brass 70d V443.

1277. do. stamped '162' on the back 78d V432.

1278. do. a pair of 'studs' on the back 77d V434 no2793.

1279. do. 76d V435.

1280. do. 82d V442.

1281. do. 84d V443.

1282. do. 99x68w V441.

1283. do. 101x68 V437.

1284. do. 70x70 V451.

1285. do. 75d V449.

1286. do. 80d V438.

1287. do. 79d V447.

1288. do. 68d V450.

1289. Stamped sheet brass 84d V446.

1290. 92d V433.

1291. 91d V429.

1292. 83d V430.

1293. 90d V436.

1294. 87d V439.

1295. 95d V428.

1296. Stamped and embossed sheet brass 80d V445.

1297. do. 73d V431.

1298. do. 88d V444.

1299. do. with blue glazed ceramic boss, 89d V440.

1300. Hame plate, cast with four studs on back for iron rivets 135x56 V454.

1301-1302. Oval plates, cast with four iron strips for securing to leather 69x55 V1041-2.

1303. Side strap, stitched leather, with an embossed horse, two stamped pattern brasses, and a small heart 344x92 V452.

1304. Martingale, stitched leather with brass buckle, two stamped and three stamped and embossed brasses 366x165 V492.

1305. Side straps, with two brass buckles to secure it to the back band, with two stamped heart, and cast shield, sunburst, heart and rosette pattern brasses 752x95 V453.

1306. Fly terret, cast brass with red,blue and white horsehair plume 340x114w V518.

1307. Fly terret, cast brass 82x54d V468.

1308. do. 88x60d V465.

1309. do. 85x57d V466.

1310. do. 106x51d V467.

1311. Bell terret, cast brass 130h V468.

HARNESS BELLS

1312. Cast bell metal rumbler with iron ball. Cast 'R'W' for Robert Wells of Aldbourne, Wilts. 1760-1826 48d no2078. Laycock.

1313. do, size 18, mounted on an iron bracket, 93d c215l V1187.

1314. Cast brass rumbler, polished, 80d V472.

1315. White metal sleigh bell/ rumbler 42d.

1316. Cast bell-metal bell, iron clapper missing, 85x85d V1033.

BOUNDARIES

1317. Browse hook, steel-edged blade stamped 'C. HELSON/EXETER', turned wood handle with ferule. 487l V715.

1318. do. handle with hooked end. 550l V714. From Mill Hill, Habertonford. Fielden.

1319. Stone gate socket with four worn holes for the iron pin on the heel of the gate, 415x375x170. From Portland Lane, Sheepstor, Dartmoor. Donated by Hansford Worth.

1320. Fixing for upper end of socket-hung gate, iron, wedge-shaped end 295x73x22.

1321. do., with splayed tie end 300x107x14.

WORKING THE SOIL

1322. Two-bill, iron, 402x74x72 V707 from Hartland. Donated by John Hockridge.

1323. Digging mattock, iron, fire-welded prongs 268x131.

1324. do. 300x131. This, or 1323, is probably 172/1956 'Tool said to be used for digging turnips' Brimley, Bovey Tracey. Donated by G. Price.

1325. Stubber, iron, 427x225 V708 31/1897. From Hartland, donated by A. Haynes.

1326. Stubber [said to be for digging out roots, but its true provenance is uncertain] steel blade stamped 'SCOTT & CO/LTD/ ....STEEL' mounted on wood handle 1380x92 V687.

1327. Breast plough [Spade] iron blade on wood shaft c.213l 601/1940 no.2583. Laycock.

1328. Velling or Skirting share iron, 649/1898. From Hartland, donated by A. Haynes

1329. Derby plough red-lead painted woodwork, wrought and cast iron fittings 2898x470x805 V1711 887/1918 from Hartland donated R. P. Chope.

1330. Two-way zole red-lead painted woodwork with wrought iron fittings 3003x632x875 887/1918 1927/997. From Hartland donated by R. P. Chope.

1331. Potato-ridging plough, ironwork only, largest piece 1020x64x330 V711 175/1956 no.3863. From Hartland donated by H. G. Hurrell.

1332-1333. Pair of drag-harrows, remains of red lead paint on wood frames, iron fittings 1425x1060 and 1405x1040 V694 1927/1004 887/1918. From Hartland donated R. P. Chope.

SOWING

1334-1335. Dibbling irons, iron with ash handles V718 830x121, V719 828x121.

1336. Seedlip [Zellup] galvanised iron sheet, a round yellow and black printed paper label on the front reads: 'WILMO... LONG LIFE & GOOD SERVICE' 625x442x 195 V717 571/1970. From Combe Fishacre. Donated by P. Farman.

1337. Fiddle drill, red-painted pine? with black linework, iron and hardwood fittings, canvas hopper and webbing sling. Stencilled on the back 'ANKESTER & Co/44 SOMNER STREET/LONDON SE/PATENTED' c.510x195 bow 968l V712.

1338. Bird clapper, oak, leather thongs 237x100x29 V1005 no.2060. Laycock.

1339. Bird scaring rattle, oak, beech etc. with metal weighting 204x61x227.

HARVESTING

1340. Reap hook, steel-edged blade, replaced turned hardwood handle, 577l V1303.

1341. Scythe, ash with iron fittings and steel-edged blade. c.152l 487/1965. Donated by H. G. Shepherd.

1342. Scythestone 295x43x35 V1299.

1343. Tathing hook, square-section iron, turned beech handle with brass ferrule 345l V688.

1344. do. ash? handle 392l V687.

1345. do., round-section iron, elm handle 468l V1295.

1346. do., turned wood handle with iron ferrule 523l V716.

1347. do. pine? handle 545l V1296.

1348. Hay [Errish] rake, ash with pine head 2290x1613. From Hartland, donated by John Corey.

1349. do. red-lead painted ash? and iron teeth 1725x1306.

1350. Potato digger, fire-welded wrought iron 252x c.172 V1291. Donated by West Cornwall Field Club.

1351. Fork [Peek], wrought iron head and ferrule on wooden shaft 1826x45.

1352. do. 1659x69 V1761.

1353. Pitchfork, wrought iron head only, 385x175 V1285.

1354. Corn dolly, 430l 381/1962. Donated by Miss Norrington.

1355. do. 280l 381/1962. Donated by Miss Norrington.

FLAILS [DRASHLES]

1356. Pine, holly and rawhide 1141&840 V695. Probably from Hartland. Donated by John Cory.

1357. Pine, holly, horn and rawhide 705&770 V1683 612/1896. From Thorverton. Donated by G.Way.

1358. Ash, holly, horn and rawhide 1107&767 V696.

1359. Pine, unidentified hardwood, horn, leather and rawhide the shaft stamped 'James Finla...' 1248&870 V1685.

1360. Pine, holly, bent wooden kibble and rawhide 100&890. Used at Lower Tor Farm, Poundsgate, in 1934. Fielden.

1361. Ash shaft with iron swivel and bound wooden kibble, blackthorn flail, rawhide middle band 990 & 958 545/1968. Donated Miss Crump, who thought it came from Oxfordshire.

1362. Flail stick, holly and rawhide, 775l V1686, may be the one cut in 1850 and donated by C. Shapley.

1363. Flail hand-shaft, ash, top turned to form a swivel 1145l.

BARLEY AWNERS [PILERS]

1364. Square iron frame, oak? shaft 1145x337x325 1927/1008 887/1918 from Hartland. Donated by R. P. Chope.

1365. do. similar to 1364 but handle missing 355x345x288.

1366. do. 354x296x363. Donated by Hansworth Worth.

1367. do. 330x189x495 V689.

1368. Round iron frame, oak? shaft 360x827d V721 1927/1009. From Hartland, donated by J. T. Haynes.

WINNOWING

1369. Blind sieve [Zemmet] nailed ash hoop with bottom of cleft wooden strips woven in a twill pattern 105x495d V722. Donated by Miss Crosscombe.

1370. Coopered vessel, described as a 'zemmet' in the museum records, but may also be a bushell grain measure oak, riveted iron bands and handles 275x445d V713.

1371. Fan, wood with iron fittings frame 709x1293x1167. From Hartland, donated by A. Squance.

1372. Winnowing machine, mahogany, with incomplete iron and brass fittings and perforated screen 610x349x625 V723 617/1940 no,2625 'from a Devon farmhouse'.

1373. Malt shovel, sycamore blade bolted to ash handle 1090x1320 581/1972. From Lincoln donated by N. Patrick.

GRAIN ETC. MEASURES

1374. Ash with iron bands, stamped 'GALLON' and 'IMPERIAL MEASURE', with crowned 'VR' and arms of the City of London branded inside 185x198d.

1375. do. stamped 'HALF GALLON' and 'GR' 192x110d. V841.

1376. do. nailed construction, branded with crowned 'VR 409' and 'QUART' 105x137d V986.

1377. Turned beech? branded 'LCA' on side 169x85d V828. Laycock.

WEIGHTS

1378. Carved granite with iron ring, carved '56' for half a hundredweight 250x260d.

1379. Pebble with iron ring, carved '14' for a stone weight 150h.

MILLSTONES

1380. Granite stone with square iron lining to cental hole 140x1101d 374/1962 from Old Flete Mill, Union Street, Torquay, demolished 1962. Donated by International Stores.

1381-1382. Pair of granite millstones, bedstone 95x570d runner 115x570d 'from the West Country'. Donated Mrs Jennings.

SHEEP: SHEPHERD'S CROOKS

1383. Wrought iron 575x31d V1736.

1384. do. 189x19d.

1385. do. 289x27d V1738.

1386. Polished steel 180x24d V1737.

1387. do. 180x24d V3205 made from the barrel of an old muzzle-loading gun by Mr Mitchell of the Pyecombe smithy, near Brighton, which had a centuries-old reputation for making the finest shepherd's cooks in southern Britain. Purchased by Mrs Fielden.

SHEARS

1388. Steel 333x86 V1188.

BELLS

1389. Sheet iron riveted clucket 125x77x75 V552.

1390. do. 140x100x76 V551.

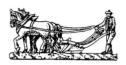
1391. do. 58x56x28 V314 Continental?

1392. Bell-metal bell 109d on elongated iron collar 390h V1004.

1393. do. 70d on round iron collar 219h V1002.

DIPPING HOOK

1394. Iron head, shaft missing 544x401.

MARKING IRONS

1395. Wrought iron star of David 220x105d V1188.

1396. do. 'SB' 392x166x112 V1184.

1397. do. 'C' 364x54x35.

1398. do. 'S' 151x106x61 V1185.

TURNIP CHOPPERS

1399. Wrought iron 1062x297 V1290

1400. do. 368x273d, V1690 (also may have been used to chop gorse for feed). L286 Laycock.

CATTLE EQUIPMENT

1401. Bull leader, iron, 191x85 V1281

1402. Castrating clam, iron, 331x91 V1286. 631/1897. From Hartland, A. Haynes.

1403. Cow bell, sheet iron, riveted, with wooden clapper 152x104x328. Probably collected from Dorset by Mrs Fielden.

1404. do. 121x88x250 provenance as 1403.

1405. do. 878x72x198 prov. as 1403.

1406. Turnip chopper, hardwood with iron blades and fittings, 1243x530x735 V1726

1407. do. elm? bench top 530x164x650h one leg missing V1725 from Ashhill Farm, Bishopsteignton, donated Mrs W. H. Dawe, July 1921.

1408. Furze hook, for cutting gorse, for feed etc., steel-edged iron 484l V960 no.2412, donated by the West Cornwall Field Club.

1409. Furze hitcher, wrought iron, 390x41d V1287 no.2413. Donated by the West Cornwall Field Club.

DAIRYING: MILKING

1410. Piggin, coopered oak with riveted iron bands, two-handled 307x325d V675.

1411. do., one handle, 370x240d V1326.

1412. do., oval, 322x278x245 V674.

1413. do., round, 340x270d V1317

1414. Yoke, beech with iron fittings 890l V703 L250. Laycock.

1415. do. 900l.

1416. Milk jug, white earthenware, finely moulded to a barrel shape, with foliage scrolls to handle and spout, the base impressed with a cross and '60', all beneath a clear glaze 241x143d C775.

1417. do. unmarked, 164x91d C776.

1418. do. impressed '18' 138x79d C777.

1419. do. impressed '18' 138x79d C777.

CREAM

1420. Brass cream pan, raised, with wired edge, 140x450d V834 L15. Laycock.

1421. do. 143x463d V833.

1422. White earthenware cream pan, clear glazed, green transfer printed mark on base: 'SAFETY MILK BOWL/No 5381/09/REGISTERED SHAPE/No 537320' 80x225d V1279.

1423. Stove for cream-scalding, off-white ceramic? tempered with fine gravel, cast iron grill, iron bands now missing 590x335d. Laycock?

1424. do. in the form of a chafing dish, spun brass bowl with wrought iron fittings and turned wood handle 172x179d V1470. Laycock.

1425. do. 143x154d V1153 514/1966. Donated by C. Luxton.

1426. Cream scalding pan, spun brass with wrought iron handle, brass patch with copper rivets 528x198d.

1427. Skimmer, beech, 348x157 V1350 no.1544 26/1930. From Hallacombe Home Farm, donated by Miss Dick.

BUTTER MAKING

1428. Butter tub, coopered oak with ash bands 163 to rim x412d V1318.

1429. do. 180x390d V1319.

1430. do. ash bands replaced with iron bands 190x460 V1320.

1431. do. ash bands 193x545 V1321.

1432. Butter churn, brown salt-glazed stoneware body and lid, rouletted decorative bands 315x195d, The dasher is bored with six holes and has a replaced shaft V1200 545/1968. Miss Crump. This is from Yorkshire, probably the Calder Valley, where W. B. Crump wrote his fine volume on *The Little Hill Farm*.

1433. do. moulded glass with pressed sheet iron lid etc., brass gearing,and turned ebonised knob. 193x95x95 V1196 538/1968. A. G. Moase.

1434. do. the glass being moulded 'BUTTER CHURN 4 QT/MADE IN ENGLAND/4 IMPERIAL QUARTS', alloy gearing cast 'BLOW' and beech paddles. V648 538/1968. A. G. Ogilvie.

BUTTER WORKING

1435. Scoop, beech 248x112 V1025/1. Laycock.

1436. do. 252x115 1025/2. Laycock.

1437. Butter beaters 417x46 and 396x48 V1334/1-2.

1438-9. Scotch hands, beech 224x78 and 2299x75 V1351/1-2 476/1965. Donated by Mrs Morris Williams

1440. do. 225x74 V1351/3.

1441. do. 225x76 V1026.

1442. Bowl used to hold the butter before shaping 135x440d V1314. Laycock.

BUTTER PRINTS

1443. Rectangular, sycamore 246x57x121 V1340 664/194? no.2763. Donated by E. H. Lane.

1444. do. 173x51x64 Vi335 no.2764.

1445. Round, sycamore 45x129d. Laycock.

1446. do. 63x50d V1358.

1447. do., in case, 119x95d V1468.

1448. do. 75x114 V1339. Laycock.

CHEESE

1449. Cheese kettle [Dish kettle] raised brass with wired edge, cast brass brackets and wrought iron bail handle 450x650d 383/1936 no.1992. Laycock.

1450. Cheese pan, raised brass with punched decoration around the rim 275x755d 383/1936 no.1991. Laycock.

1451. Cheese vat, turned elm 68x360d V1351 no.2037. Laycock.

1452. Sinker, elm? 80x236d 1927/998.

1453. Drip bowl, 'placed under the mould to catch the drip' [a curd drainer?] elm 258x268x83h V1353. Laycock.

1454. Cheese press, elm table, rough-cut posts, legs etc, iron screw 1135x [table] 355x713. Purchased from near Kingsbridge in 1900.

1455. Cheese press, dark woodwork with traces of blue paint, wrought and cast iron fittings, includung the maker's plate: 'BROWNS/PATENT/PRESS 1210x945x465 V1719.

GAMEKEEPING

1456. Spring gun, iron barrel and flintlock mechanism on hardwood stock 540l. Found at Rosemount, Compton, in 1937 798/1945. Donated H. N. Hasler.

1457. do. 505l. Laycock.

1458. Mantrap 1870x475 V1715 460/1887. From Totnes, donated R. Earle.

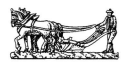

1459. do. 1345x310h 279/1935 no.1138. From Gloucestershire, donated by Miss Swinscow.

1460. do. 1224x230h.

1461. do. 289x157 V1673 L201. Laycock.

1462. do. 109x225 V1714.

1463. Trip-plate of mantrap 195x211 441/1886. From Leighon, Manaton, donated by Rev. Preb. Wolfe.

1464. Gin trap 505x150x95 no.3779. Donated by Miss Lutremouille.

1465. do. 295x120x73.

1466. do. 297x135x72 V1670 475/1965 stamped '...LINS' on spring and '9' on latch
1467. Pole trap 34x65d V1382 no.2222. Laycock.

PEAT CUTTING

1468. Fag iron [vag-ire] only the iron head 125x345x271, stamped 'G.PROUT' remains, but when collected, it had a slightly curving wooden shaft V748. From Dartmoor. Fielden.

1469. Turf iron [turf-ire] with pine shaft 1230x215x135 V1742.

1470. Slitting knife, iron blade, replaced handle 1495x73 V1743.

1471. Butting iron [spending-ire] iron blade and wooden handle 1075x247.

1472. Peat fork, wrought iron 240x99 from the Wayside Museum, Zennor, Cornwall.

THATCHING

1473. Whipping horse iron bars on wooden bows, two legs missing 1200x670. From Blackawton.

1474. Reed comb ash handle with square-sectioned iron teeth 289x192 V686.

1475. do. 306x272 V685.

1476. do. 242x257 V1756 1927/1007.

1477. do. flat-sectioned iron teeth 263x234 V1675.

1478. do. black stain on wood, 195x185 V684.

1479. Wink oak frame on untrimmed shaft, with straw rope 1005x567x64 V1760. Fielden.

1480. Straw rope twister [wimble] round iron rod with wood handles 520x165 V1752. Fielden.

1481. do. oak with iron hook 190x215 V1753.

1482. Biddle pine with iron prongs 324x527x72 V1757. Fielden.

1482. Beater [smoothing board] 538x [board]188x218 V1758. Fielden.

1484. do. handle broken off short 267x [board] 193x200 V1754.

1485. Thatcher's hook steel-edged blade, ash handle with iron ferule 555l. Fielden.

1486. Thatcher's thumb-piece, leather with string band to hold it across the palm 124x100. Fielden.

1487-8. Thatcher's strads, leather with iron buckles 327l and 317l V1765.

1489. Thatcher's comb, 8 wrought iron prongs on wooden shaft. 880x95x48. V1759.

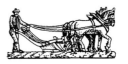

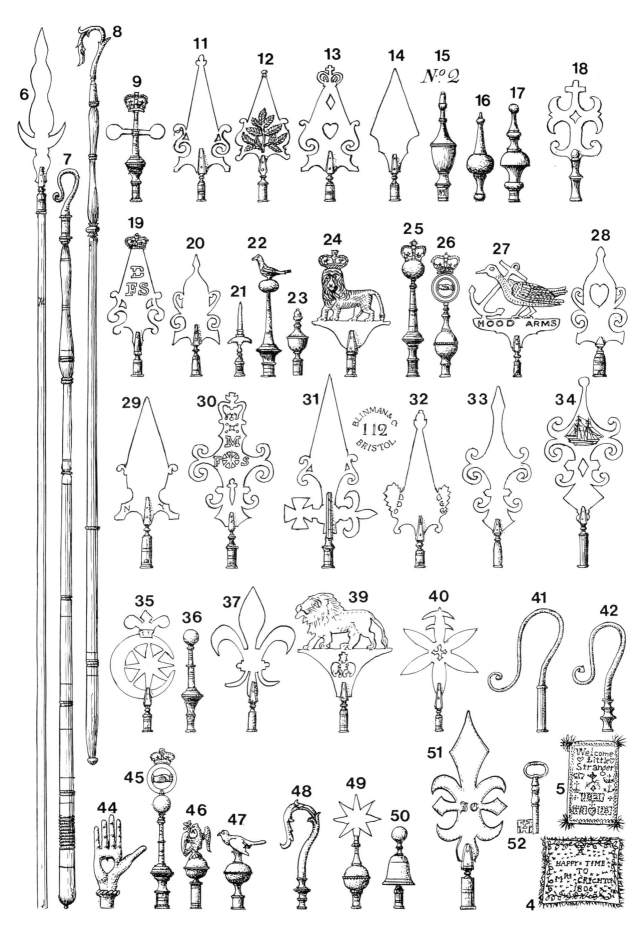

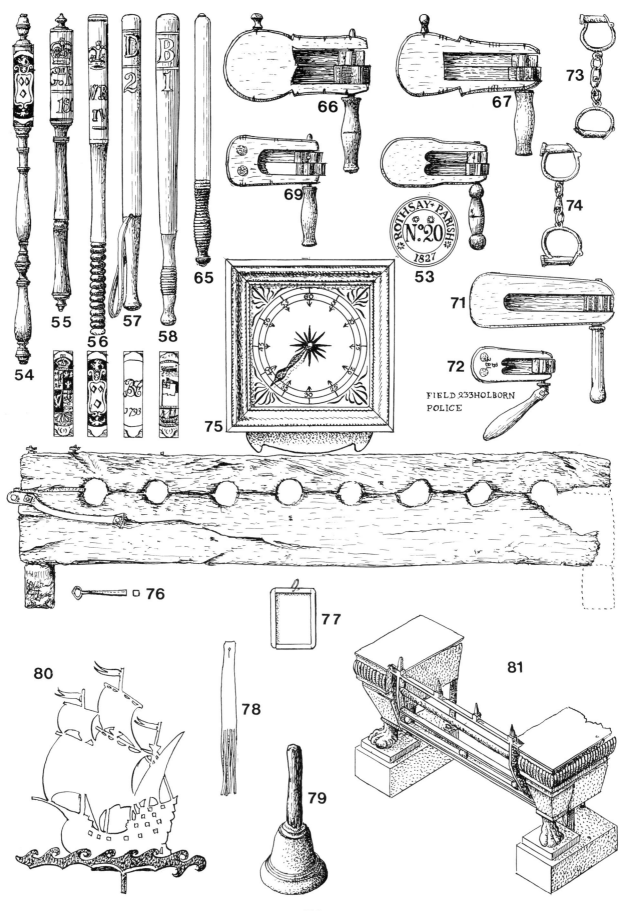

54

55

56

57

58

65

66

67

73

69

53

ROTHSAY · PARISH
Nº20
1827

74

71

72

FIELD 233 HOLBORN
POLICE

75

76

77

78

79

80

81

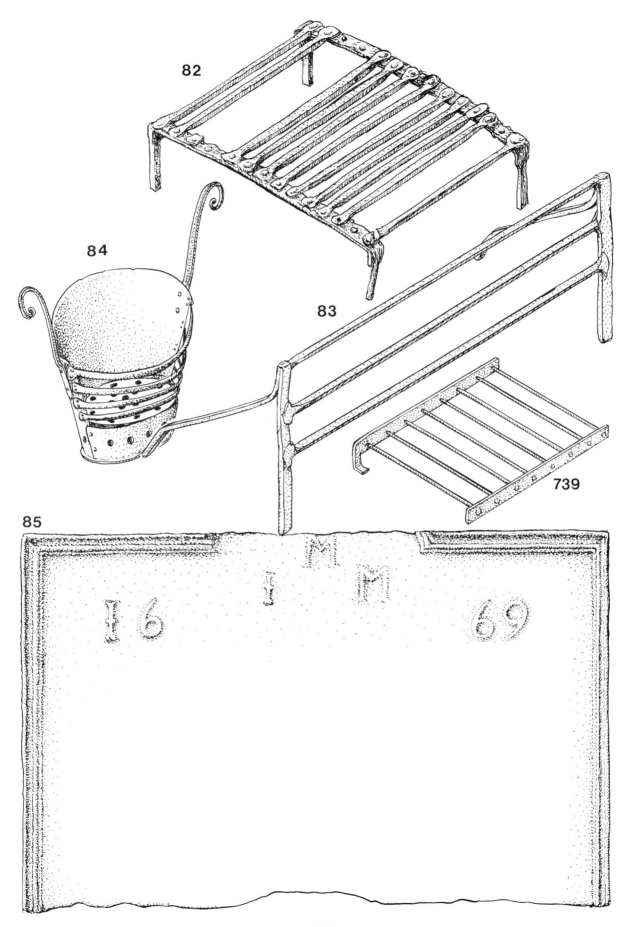

82

84

83

739

85

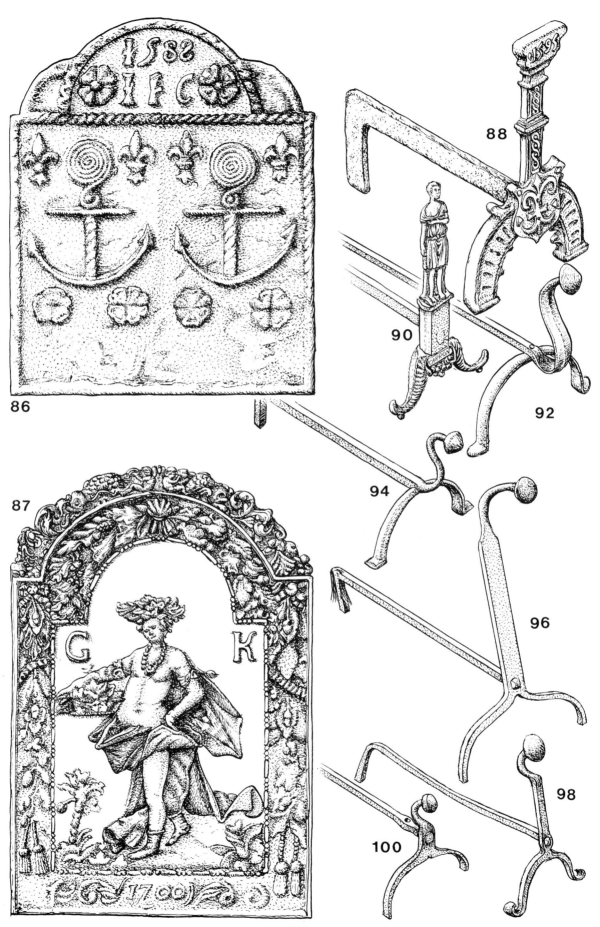

86

87

88

90

92

94

96

98

100

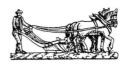

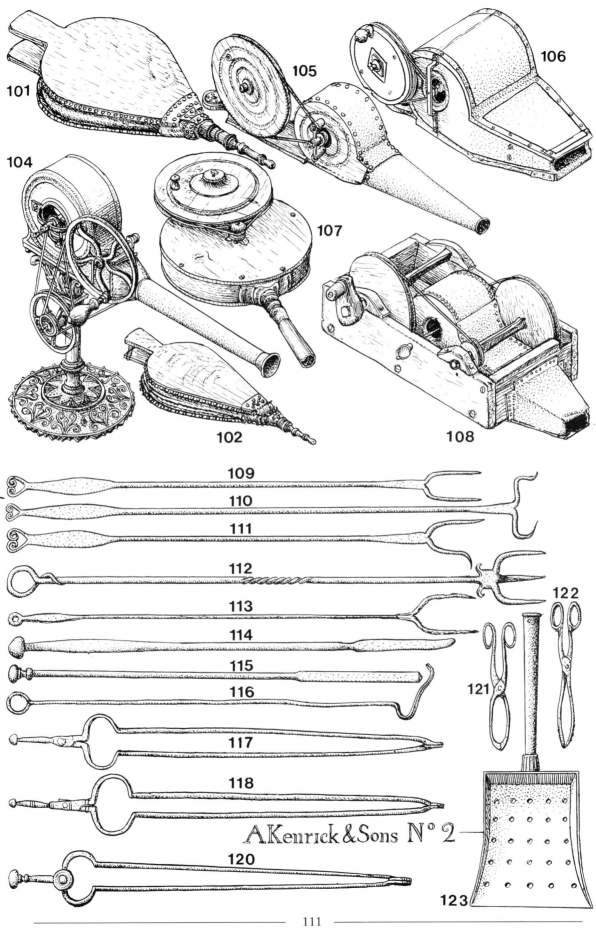

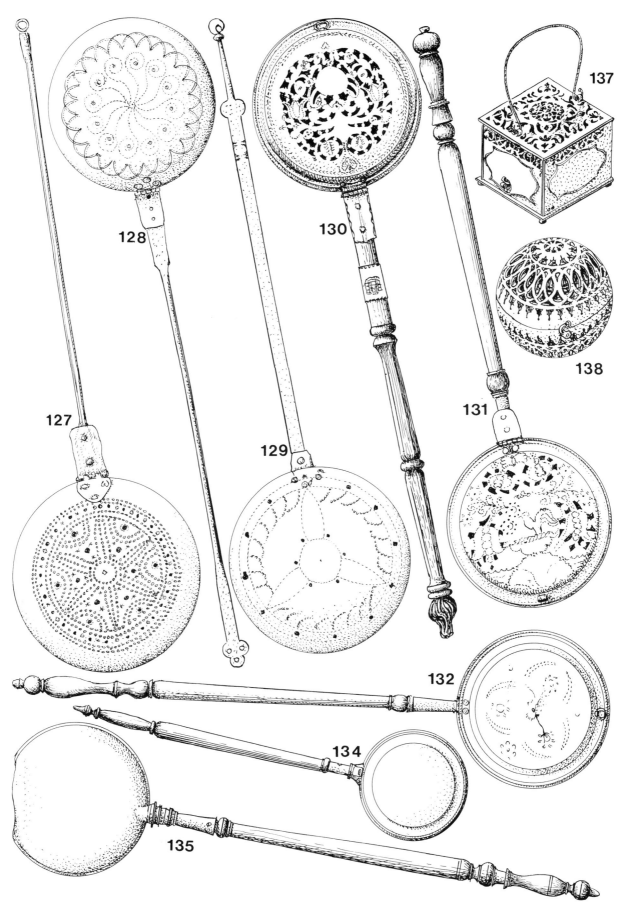

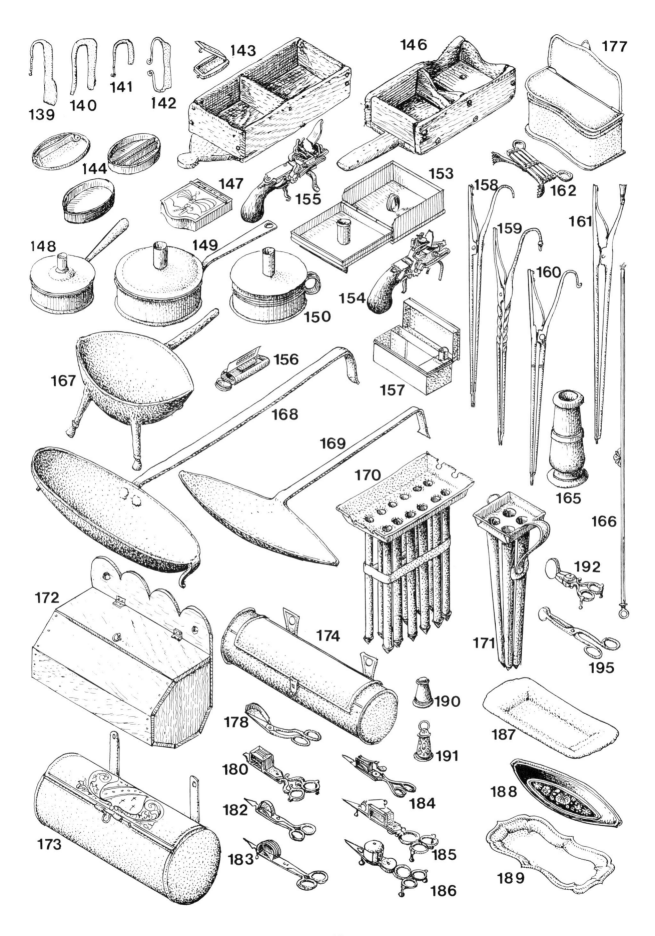

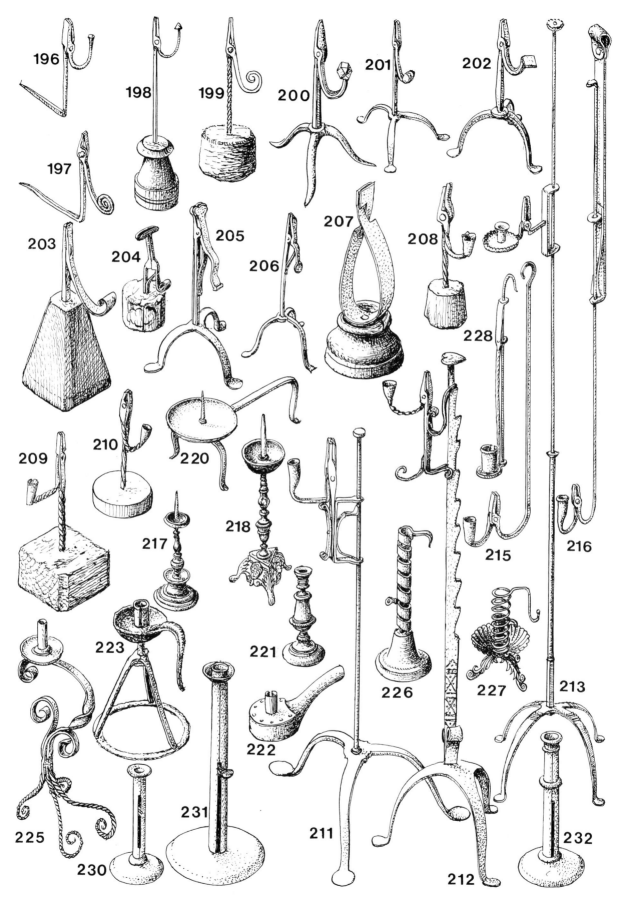

196

198

199

200

201

202

197

203

204

205

206

207

208

228

209

210

220

217

218

215

216

223

221

226

227

213

225

230

231

222

211

212

232

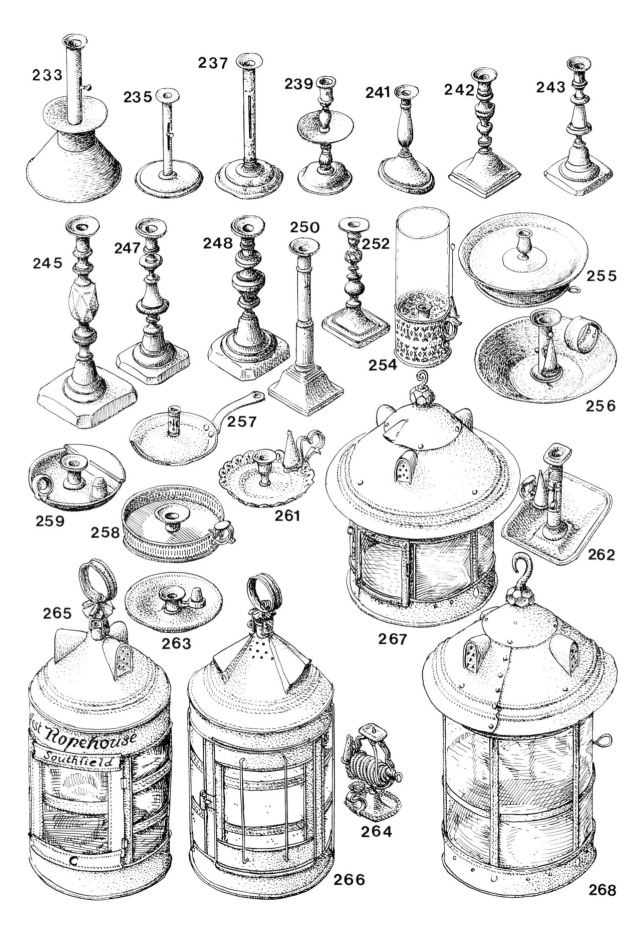

233

235

237

239

241

242

243

245

247

248

250

252

254

255

256

257

259

258

261

262

267

265

263

266

264

268

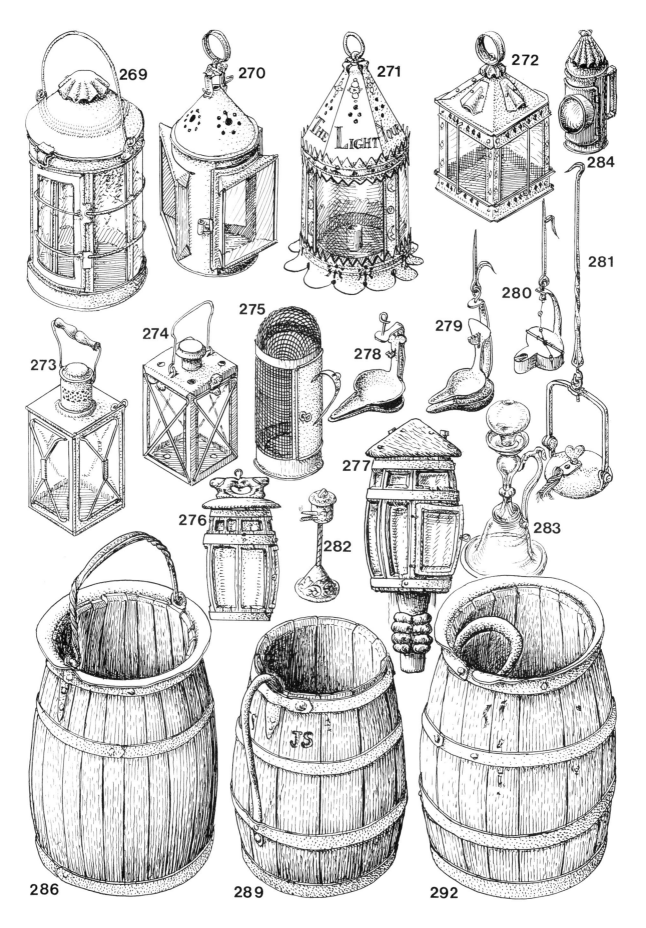

294 296 297 298

295 300 301 302 299

304 305 303

306 307

309 310 311 312

313 314 U.ALSOP 315 J.A 317

319

320

324

325

322

326

330

321

354

355

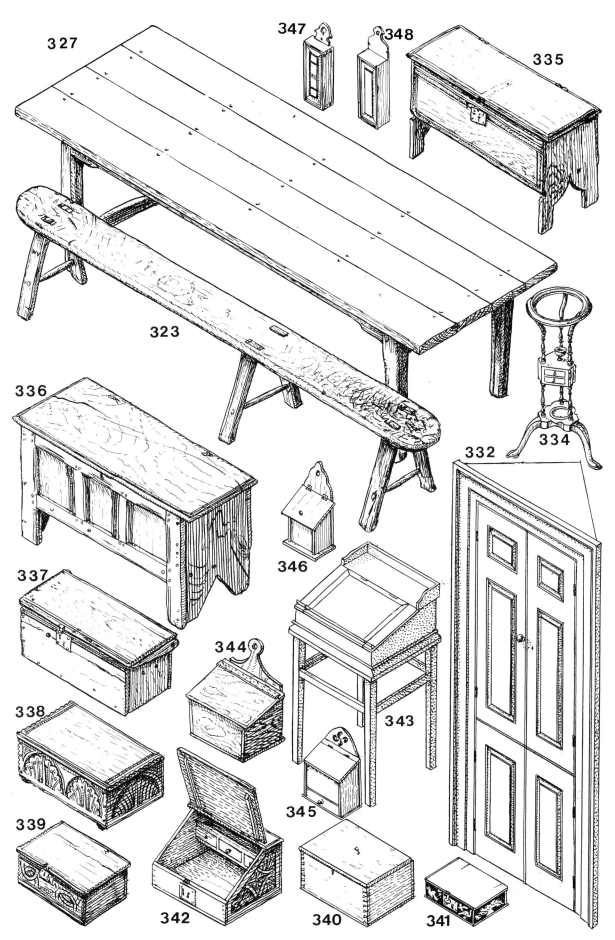

327

347

348

335

323

336

334

332

346

337

344

343

338

345

339

342

340

341

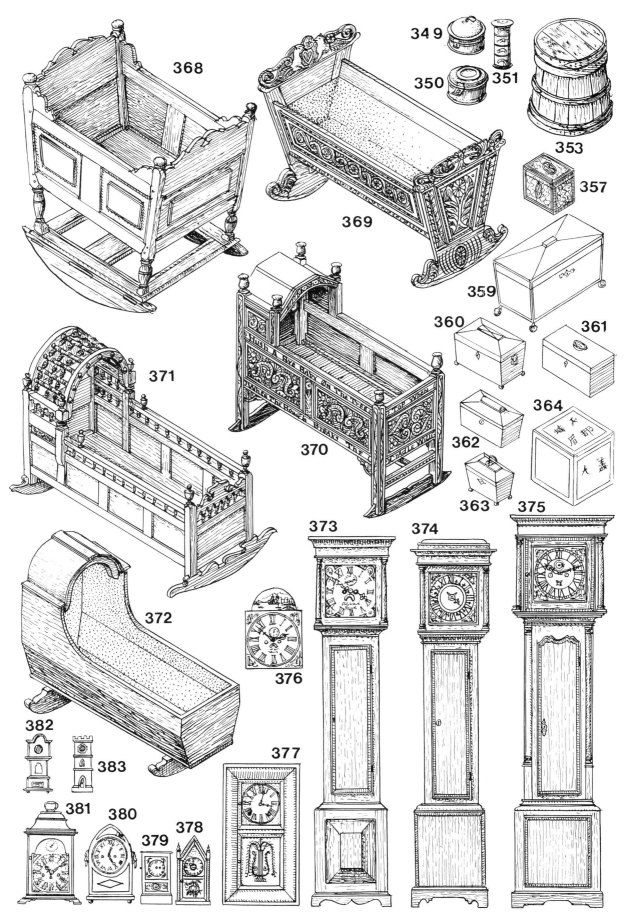

349

350   351

353

357

368

369

359

360   361

362   364

371

370

363   375

372   373   374

376

382

383   377

381   380   379   378

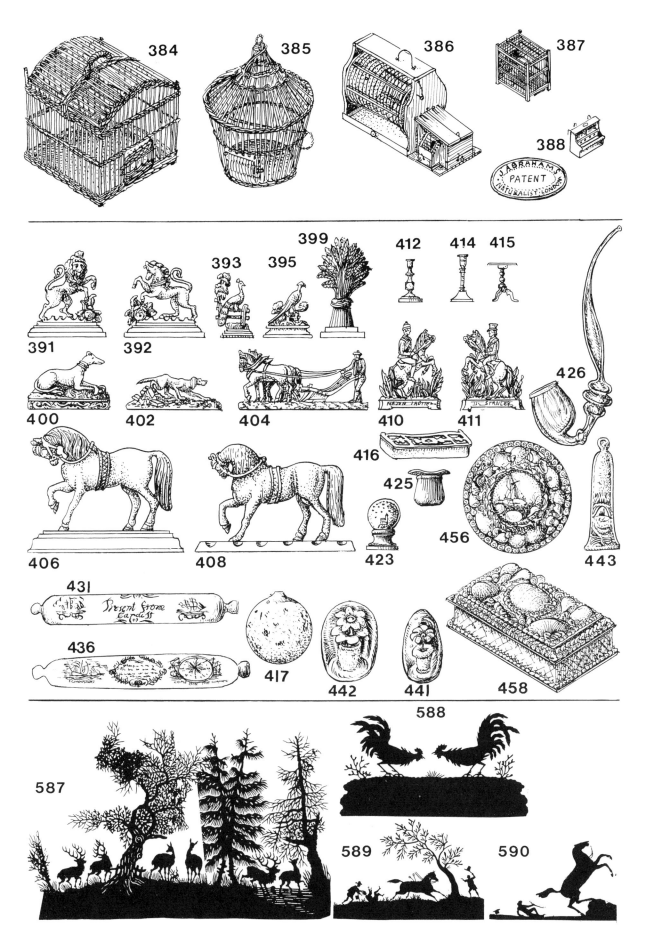

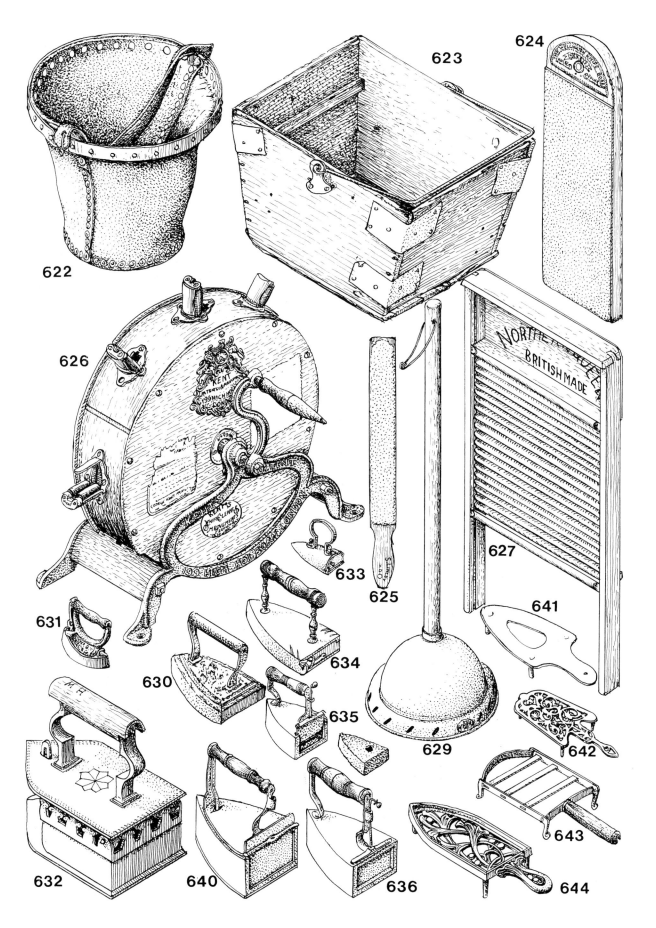

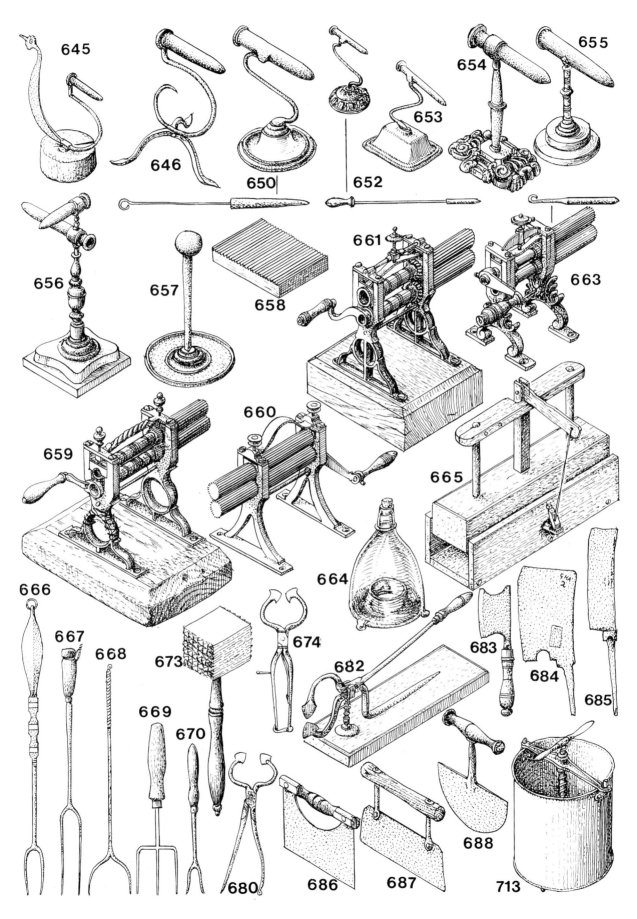

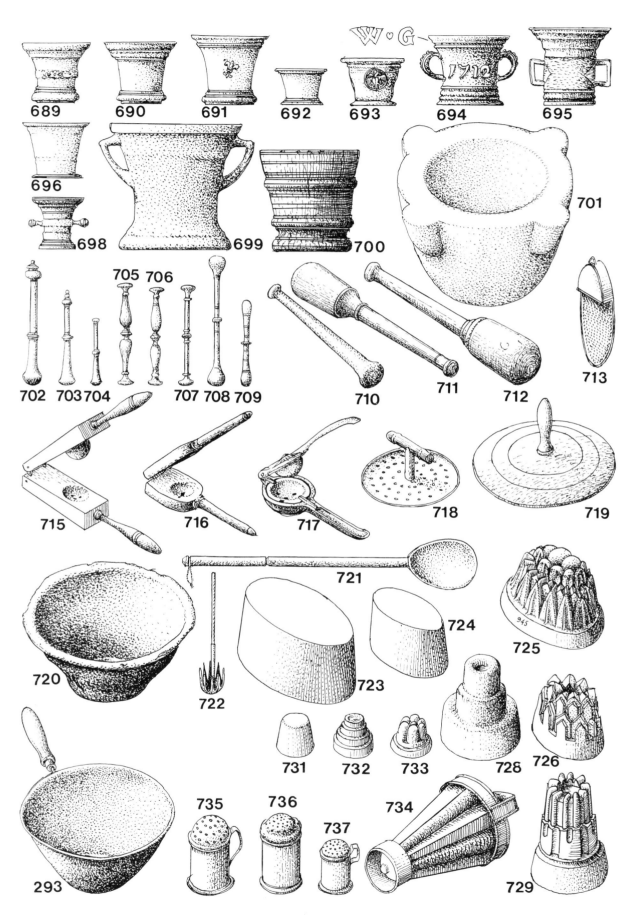

689 690 691 692 693 694 695

696 698 699 700 701

702 703 704 705 706 707 708 709 710 711 712 713

715 716 717 718 719

720 721 722 723 724 725

731 732 733 728 726

293 735 736 737 734 729

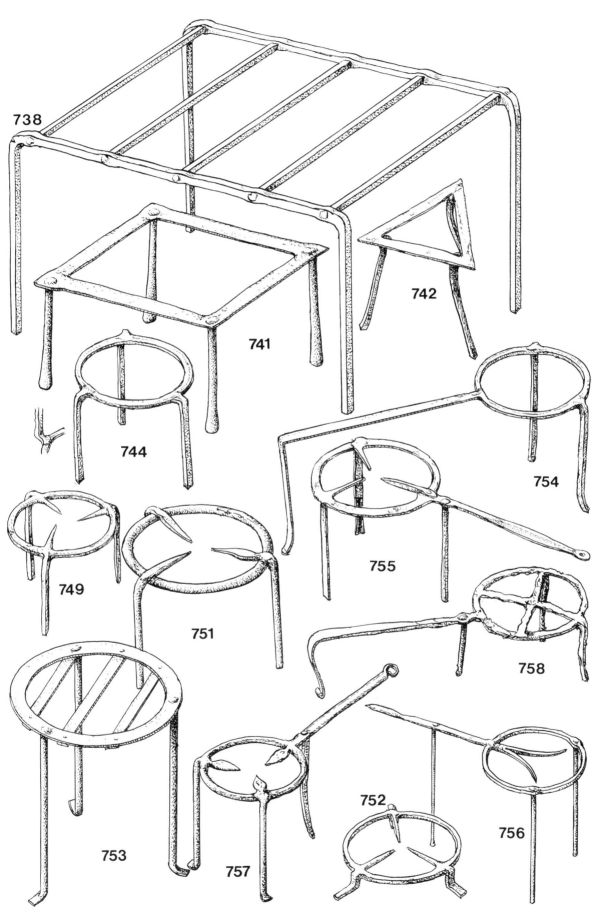

738

741

742

744

754

749

751

755

758

753

757

752

756

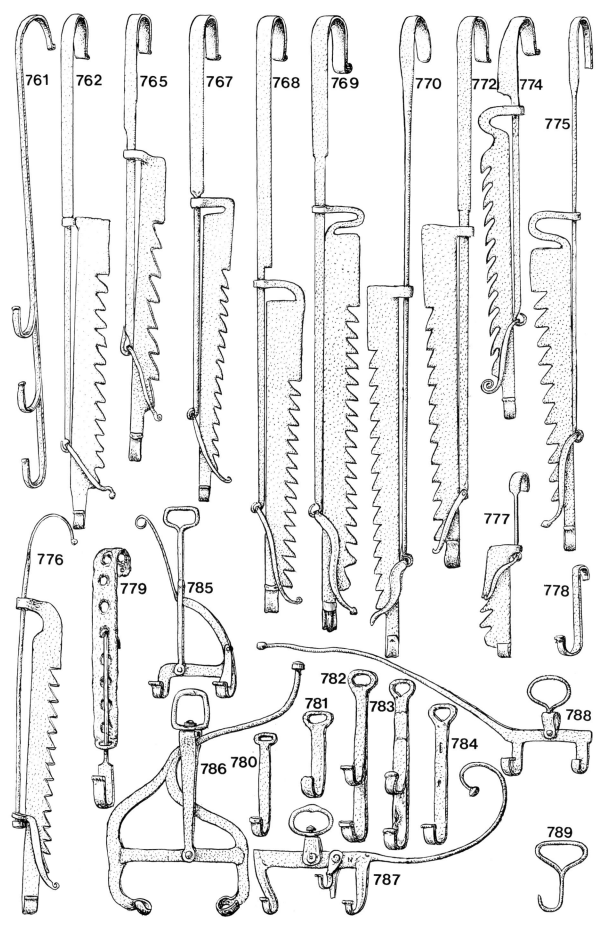

761 762 765 767 768 769 770 772 774 775

776 779 785 777 778

786 780 781 782 783 784 787 788 789

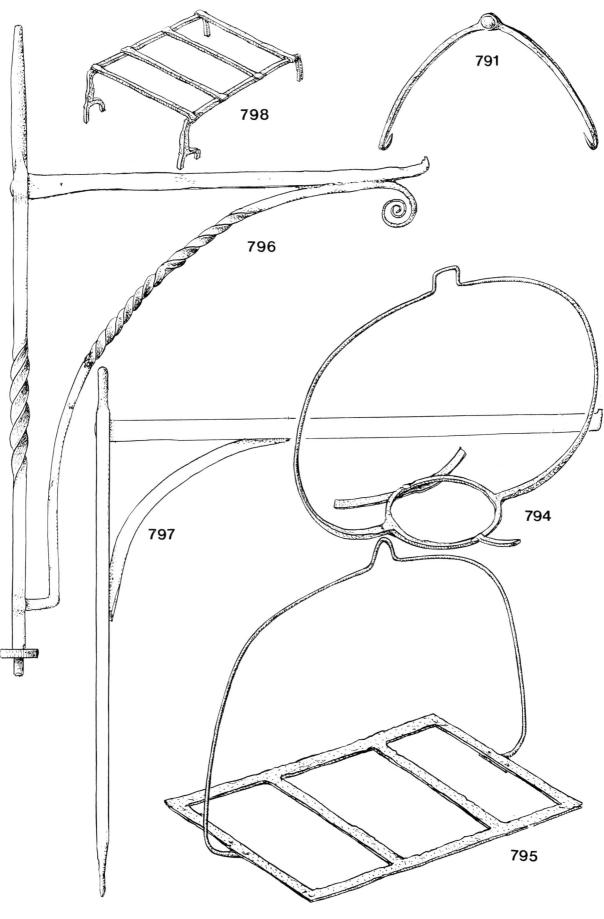

791

798

796

797

794

795

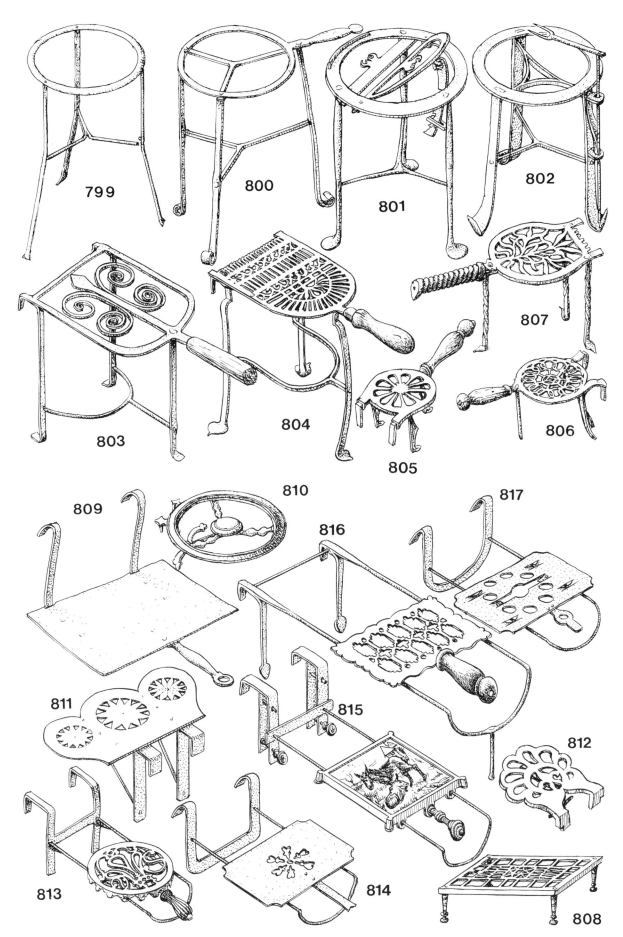

799

800

801

802

803

804

805

806

807

809

810

817

816

811

815

813

814

812

808

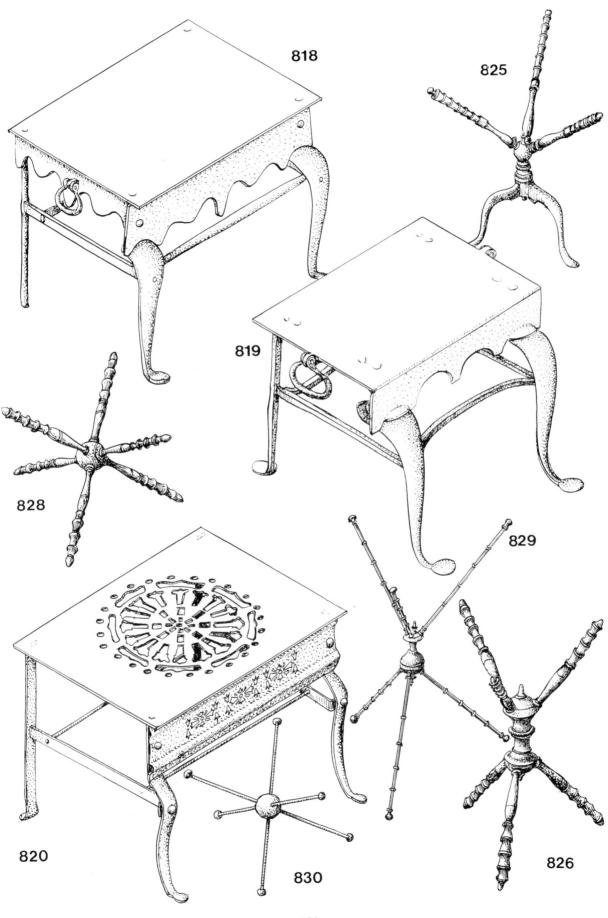

818

825

819

828

829

820

830

826

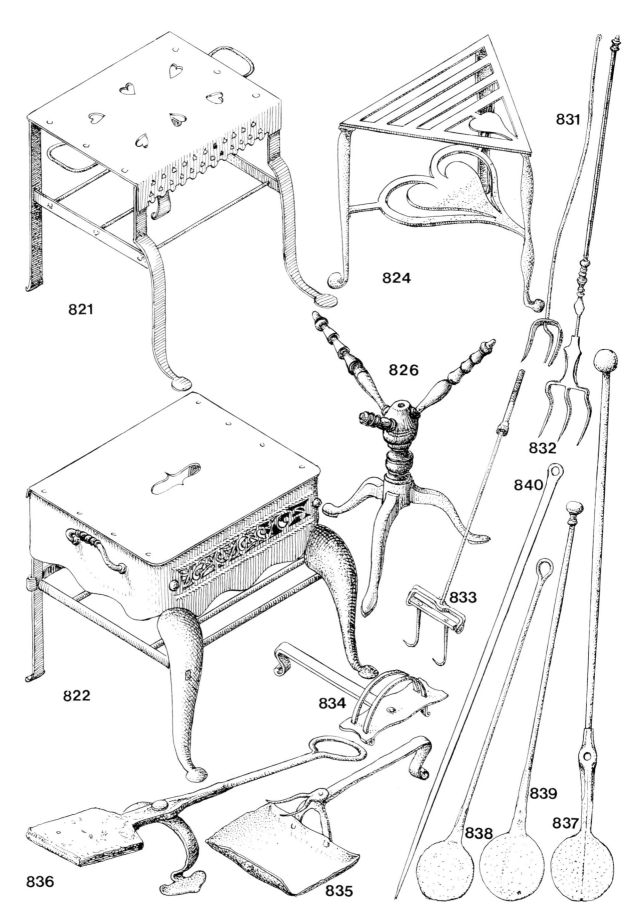

821

824

831

826

832

840

833

834

822

836

835

838

839

837

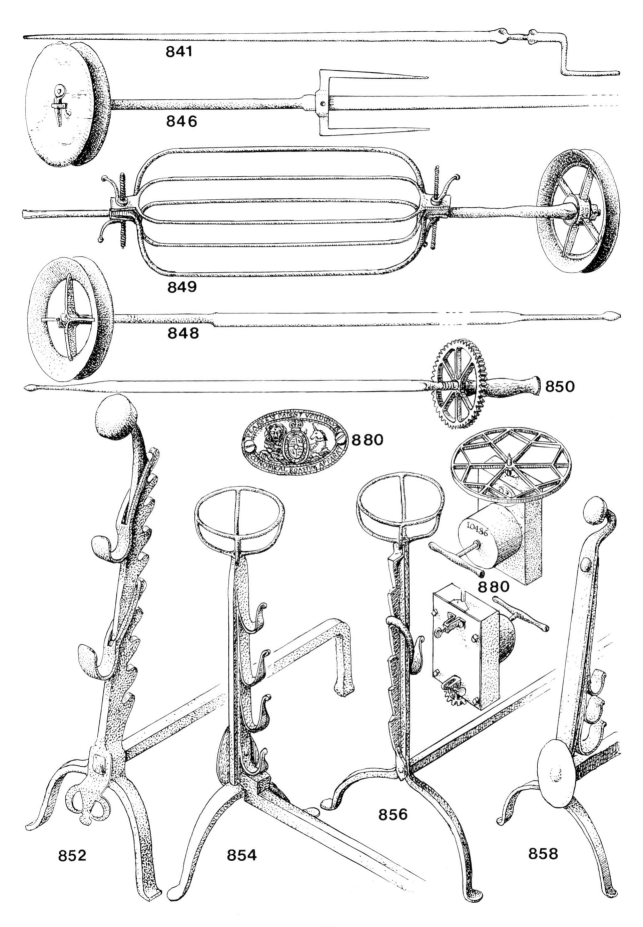

841

846

849

848

850

880

880

852

854

856

858

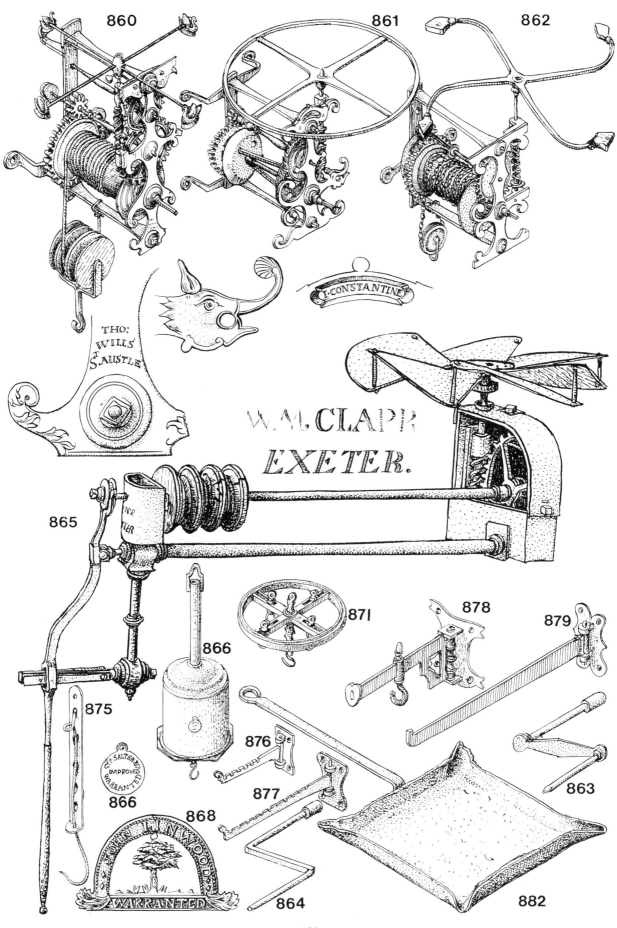

860

861

862

THO: WILLS St AUSTLE

I. CONSTANTINE

W. M. CLAPP EXETER.

865

871

878

879

866

875

876

877

863

866

868

864

882

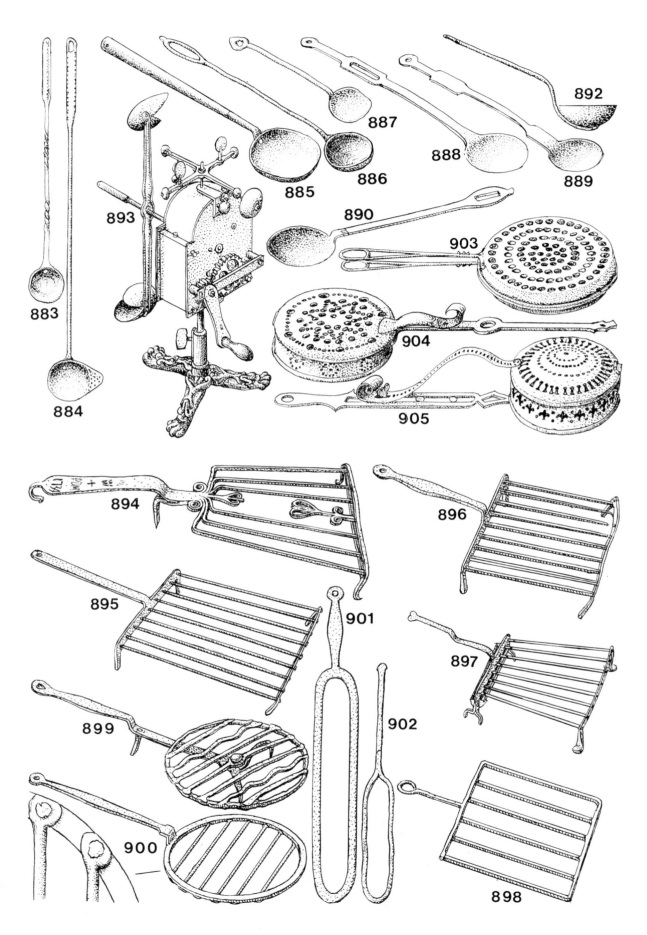

883

884

893

885

886

887

888

889

890

892

903

904

905

894

896

895

901

897

899

902

900

898

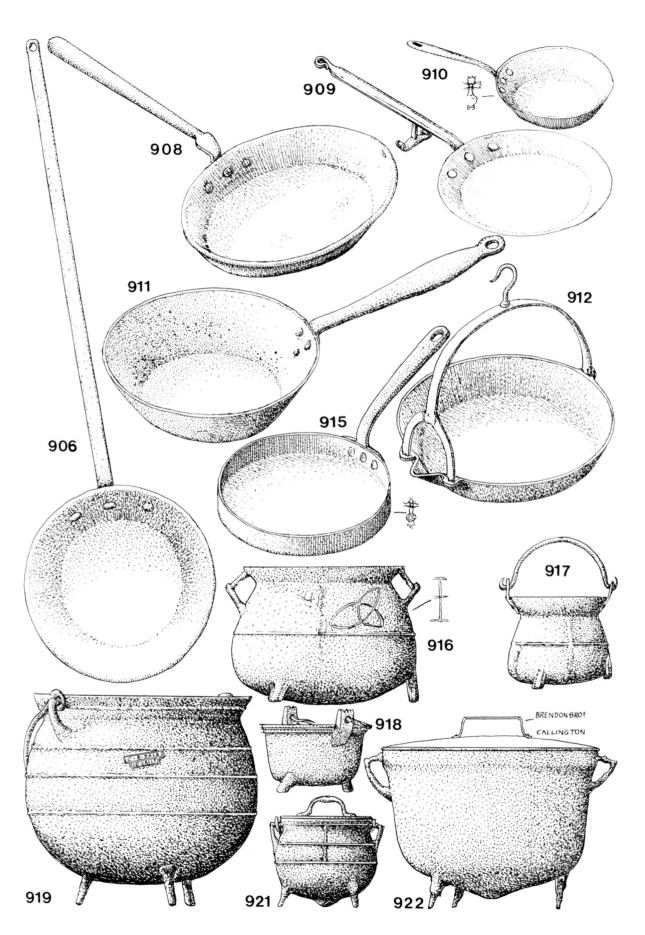

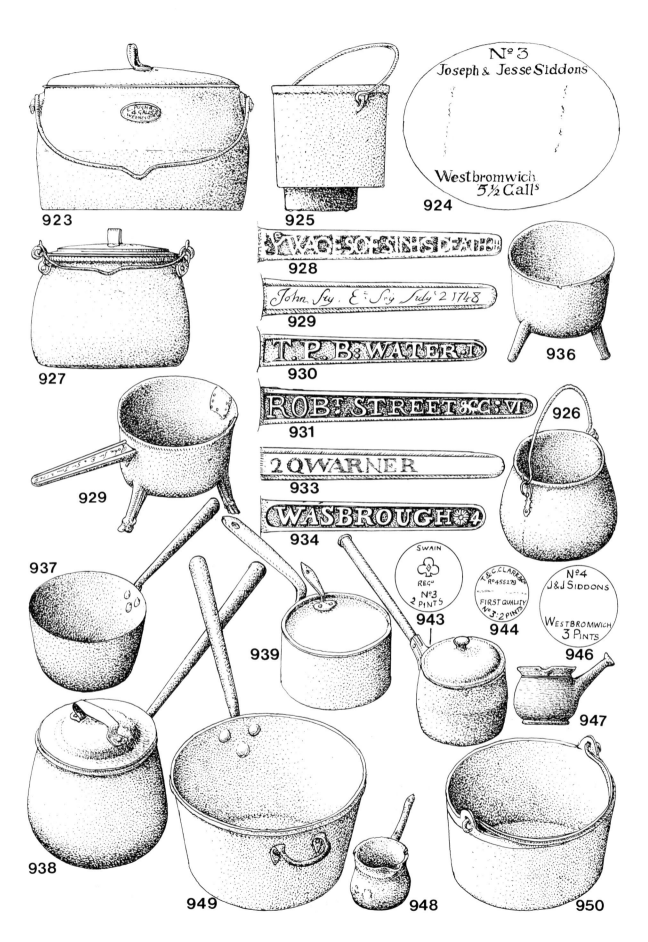

923

925

924

No 3
Joseph & Jesse Siddons

Westbromwich
5½ Gall^s

927

928

929

930

931

933

934

926

936

937

929

939

943

944

946

947

938

949

948

950

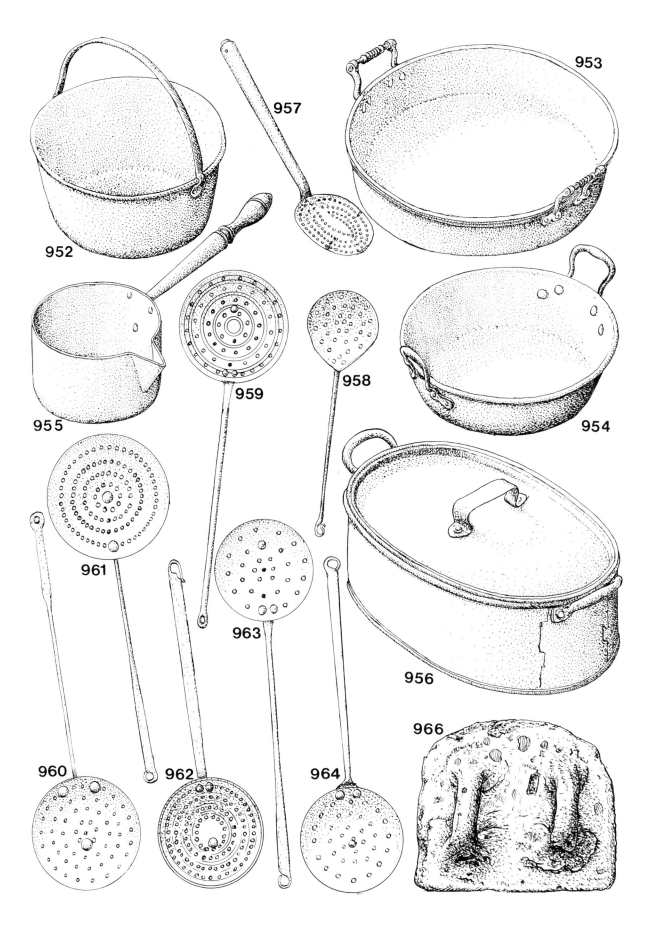

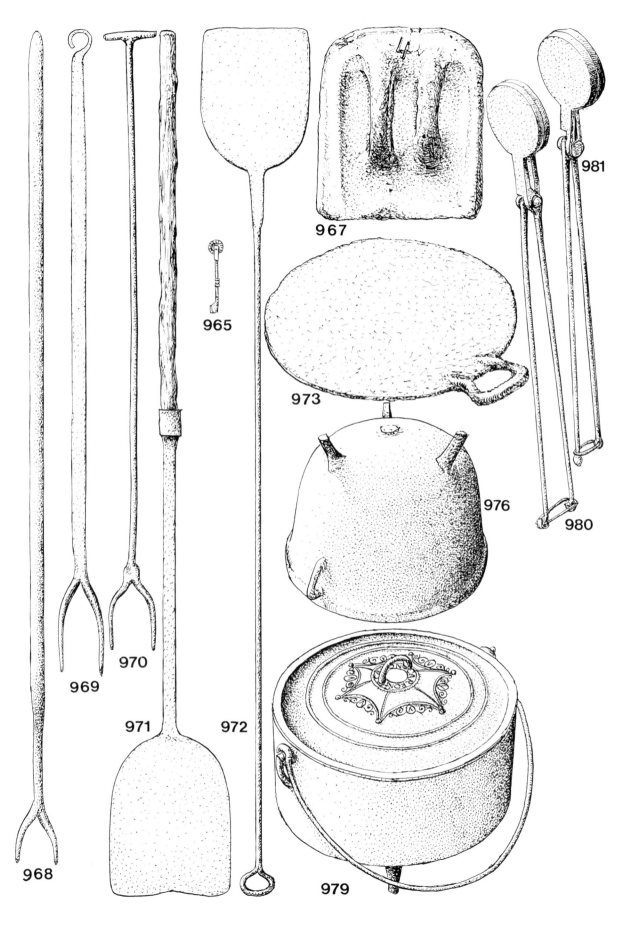

965

967

968

969

970

971

972

973

976

979

980

981

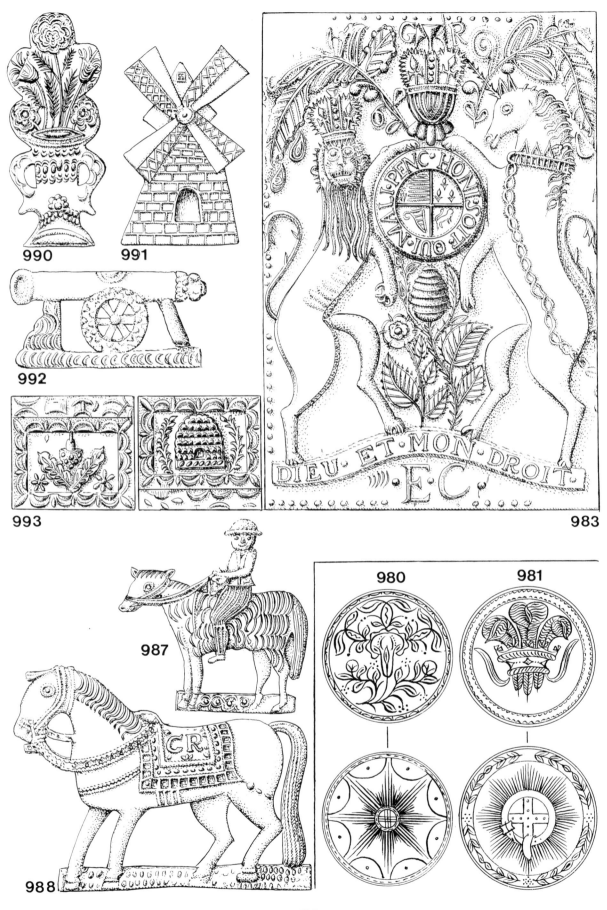

990

991

992

993

983

987

988

980　　981

2

3

985
PAUL PRY

986
W. CORDER

987

985

989

990

984

988

984

986

991
CLEANLY.

992

989

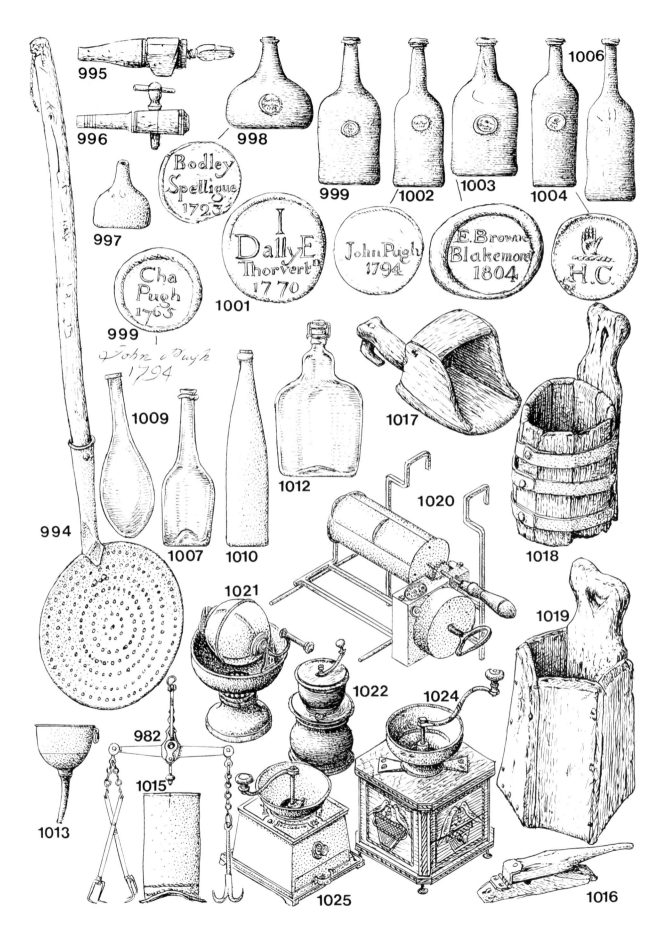

995

996

997

998

Bodley
Spellique
1723

999

1002

1003

1004

1006

Cha
Pugh
1765

I
DallyE
Thorvert"
1770

John Pugh
1794

E.Browne
Blakemore
1804

H.C

1001

999

John Pugh
1794

1009

1012

1017

1020

1018

994

1007

1010

1021

1022

1019

1024

982

1015

1013

1025

1016

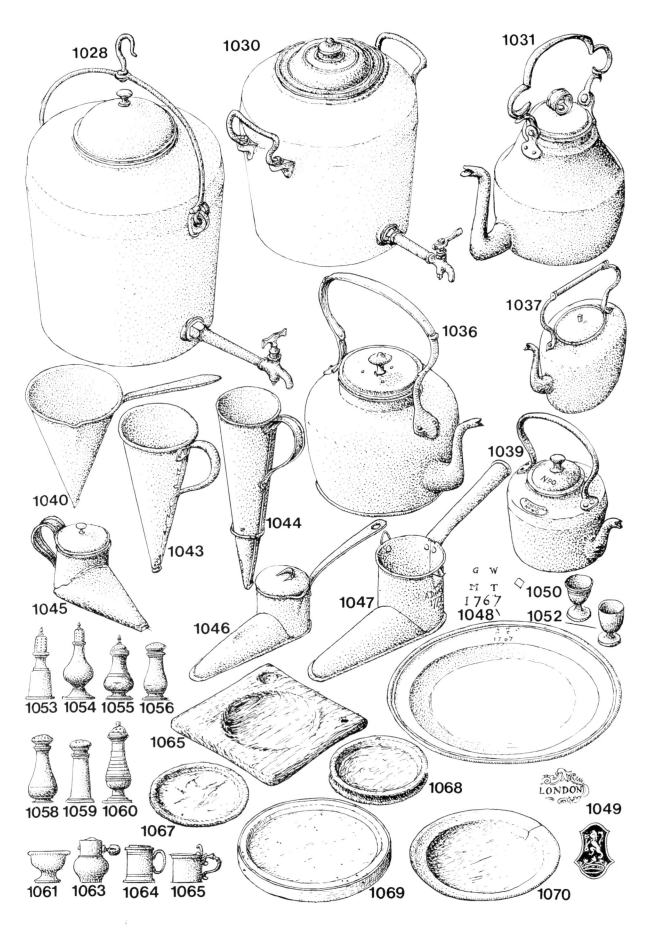

1028

1030

1031

1037

1036

1039

1040

1044

1043

1045

1046

1047

1048

1050

1052

1053 1054 1055 1056

1058 1059 1060

1065

1067

1068

1069

1049

1070

1061 1063 1064 1065

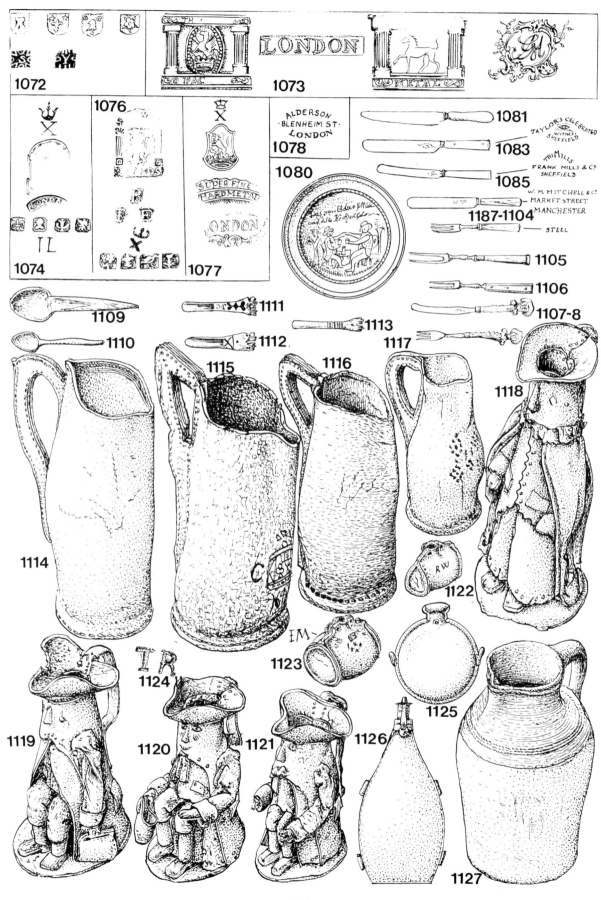

1072

1073

LONDON

METAL

1076

1078
ALDERSON
·BLENHEIM ST·
LONDON

1080

SUPER FINE
HARDMETAL

ONDON

1074

IL

1077

1081

1083

1085

TAYLOR'S CELEBRATED
WITNESS
SHEFFIELD

TRIMILLS
FRANK MILLS & CO
SHEFFIELD

W. M. MITCHELL & CO
MARKET STREET
MANCHESTER

STEEL

1187-1104

1105

1106

1107-8

1109

1110

1111

1112

1113

1117

1114

1115

1116

1118

1122

RW

1123

IM

1125

1126

1119

1120

1121

IR

1124

1127

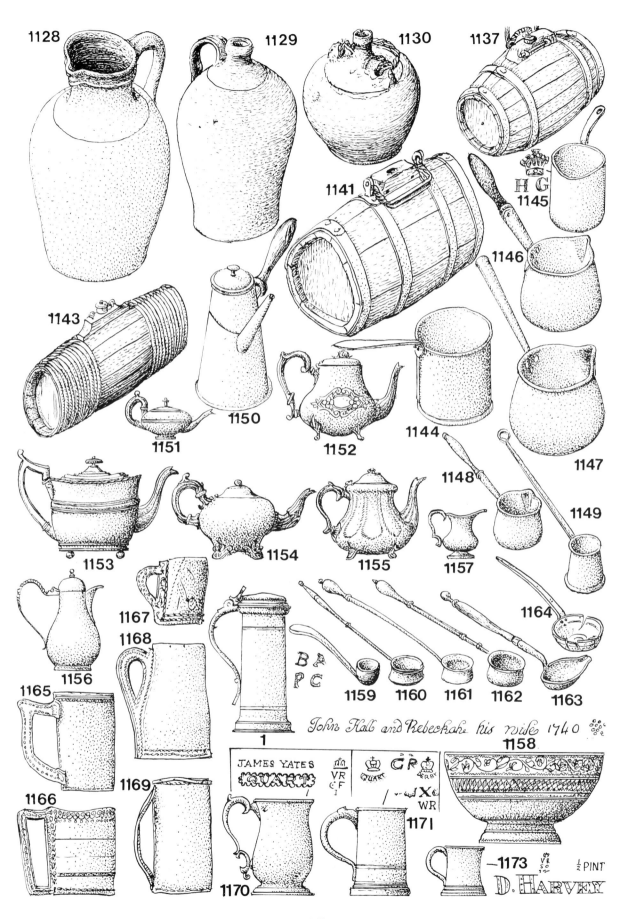

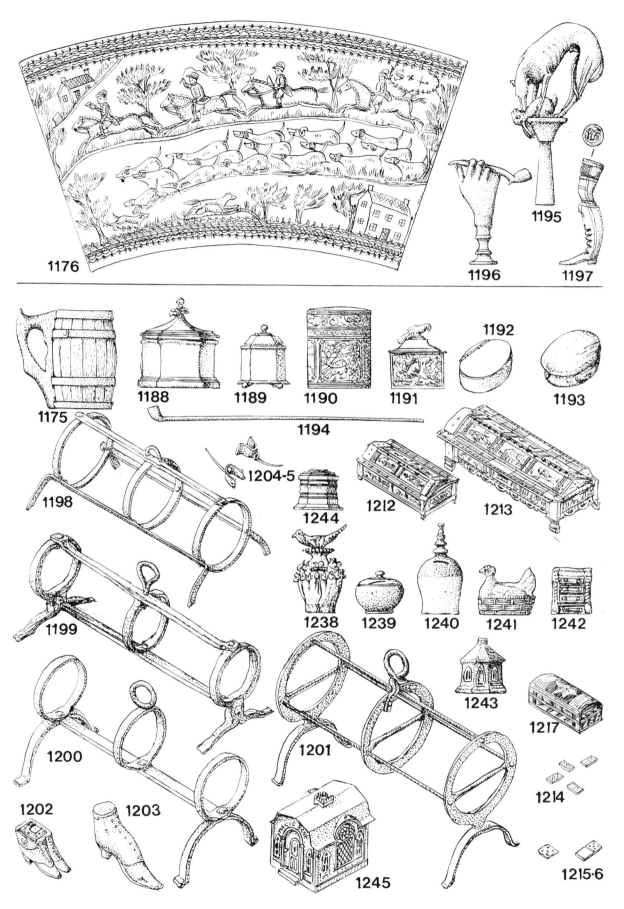

1176

1195

1196   1197

1175   1188   1189   1190   1191   1192   1193

1194

1198   1204-5   1212   1213

1244

1199   1238   1239   1240   1241   1242

1200   1201   1243

1217

1202   1203   1214

1245   1215·6

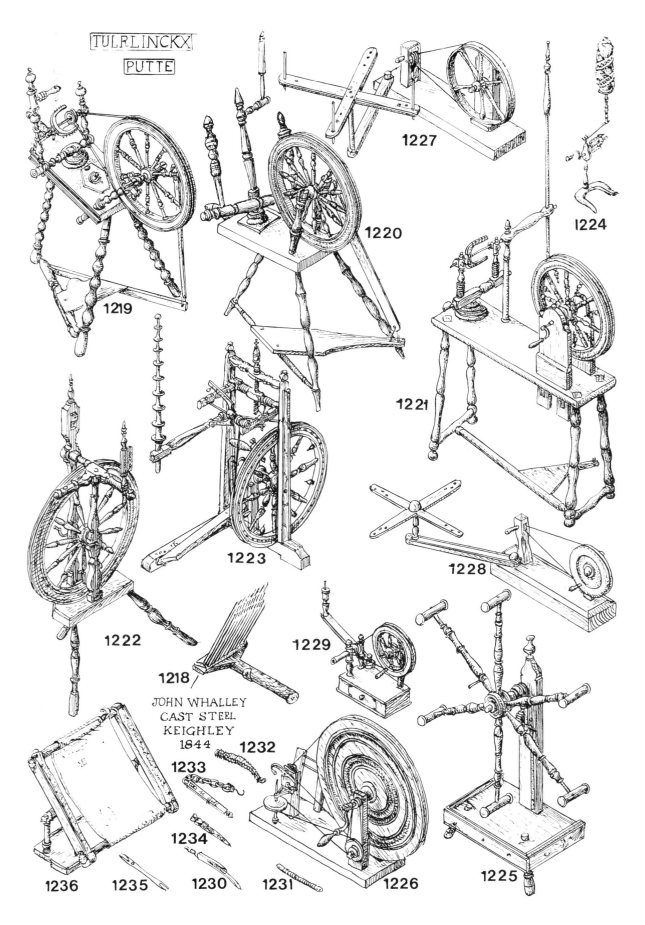

TULRLINCKX
PUTTE

1227

1220

1219

1224

1221

1223

1228

1222

1218

1229

JOHN WHALLEY
CAST STEEL
KEIGHLEY
1844   1232

1233

1234

1225

1236   1235   1230   1231   1226

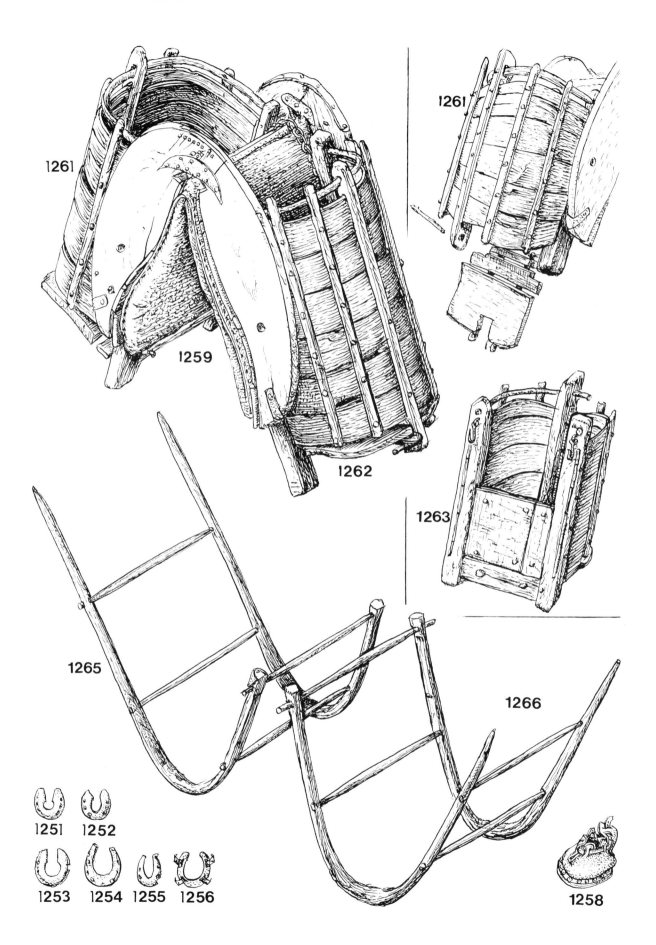

1261

1259

1261

1262

1263

1265

1266

1251 1252

1253 1254 1255 1256

1258

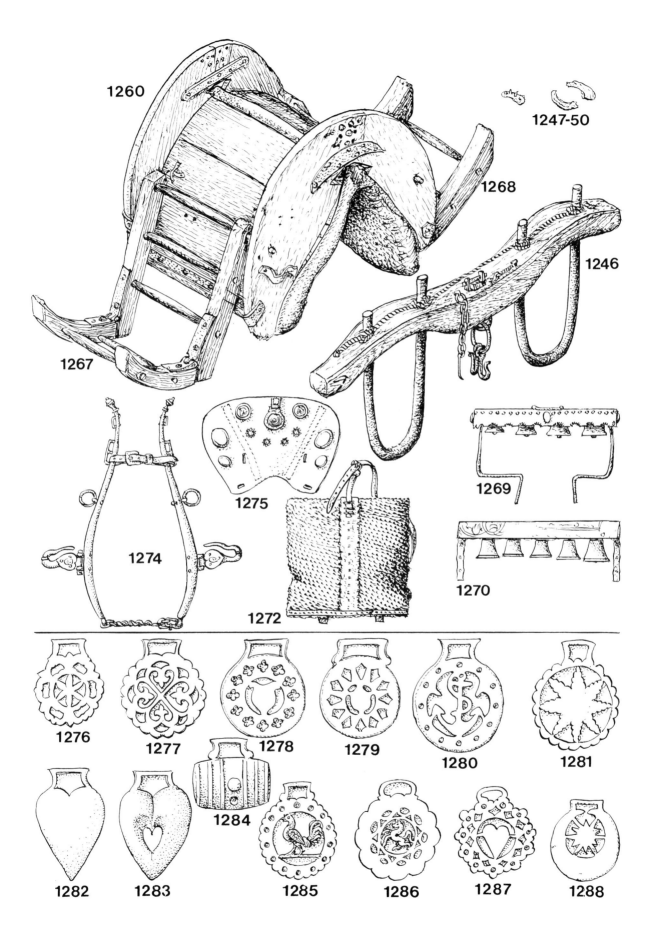

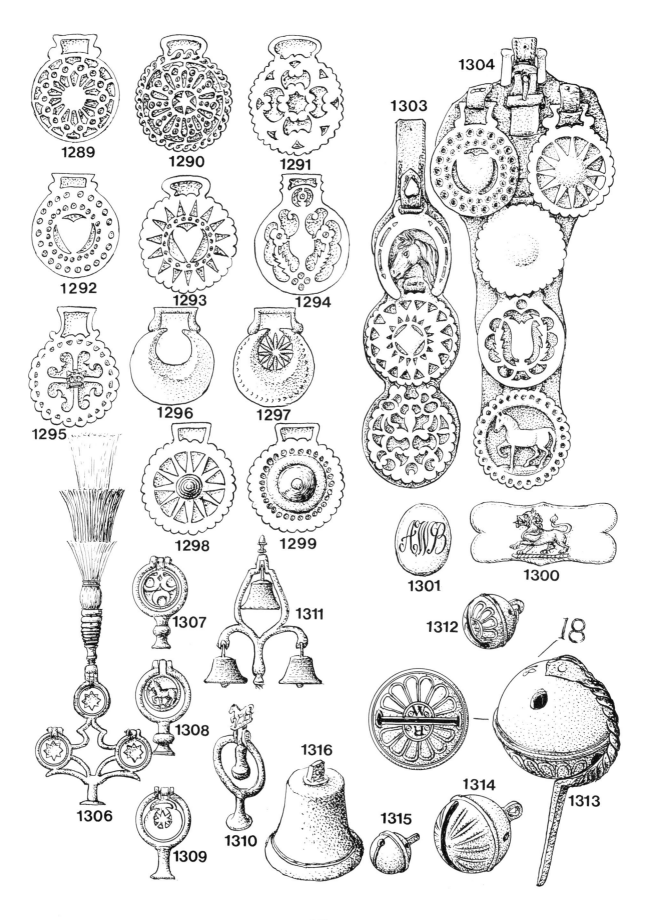

1289

1290

1291

1292

1293

1294

1295

1296

1297

1298

1299

1303

1304

1300

1301

1306

1307

1308

1309

1310

1311

1312

1313

1314

1315

1316

18

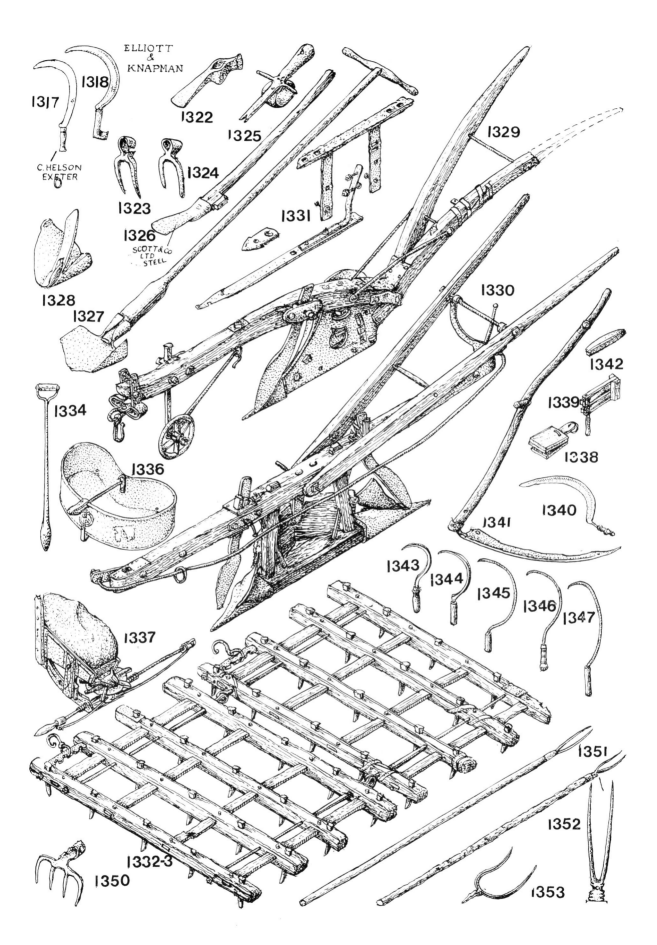

ELLIOTT
&
KNAPMAN

1317

1318

1322

1325

1329

1323

1324

C. HELSON
EXETER

1326

SCOTT & CO
LTD
STEEL

1331

1328

1327

1334

1330

1342

1339

1338

1336

1341

1340

1337

1343

1344

1345

1346

1347

1351

1352

1332-3

1350

1353

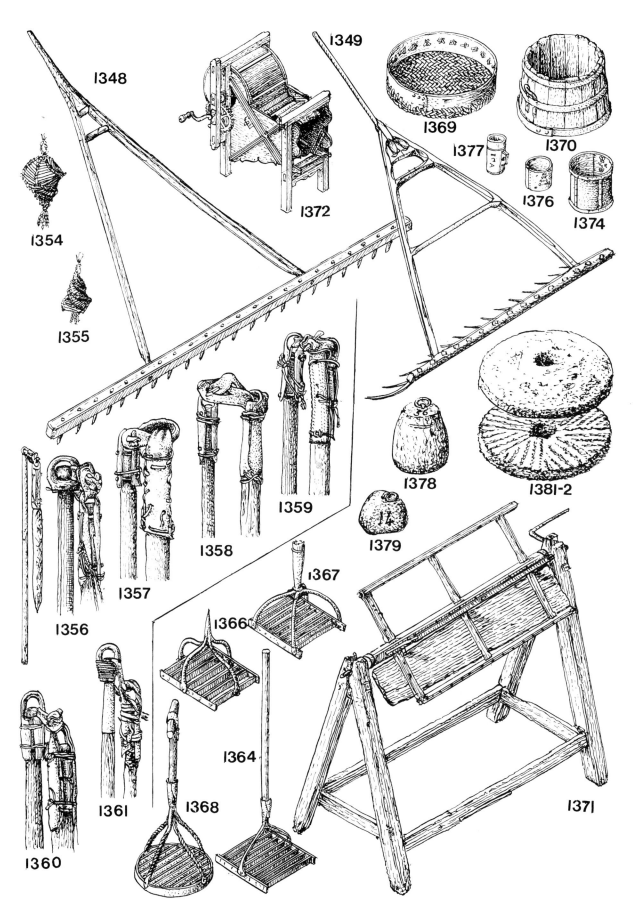

1348

1349

1354

1355

1356

1357

1358

1359

1360

1361

1364

1366

1367

1368

1369

1370

1372

1374

1376

1377

1378

1379

1381-2

1371

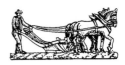

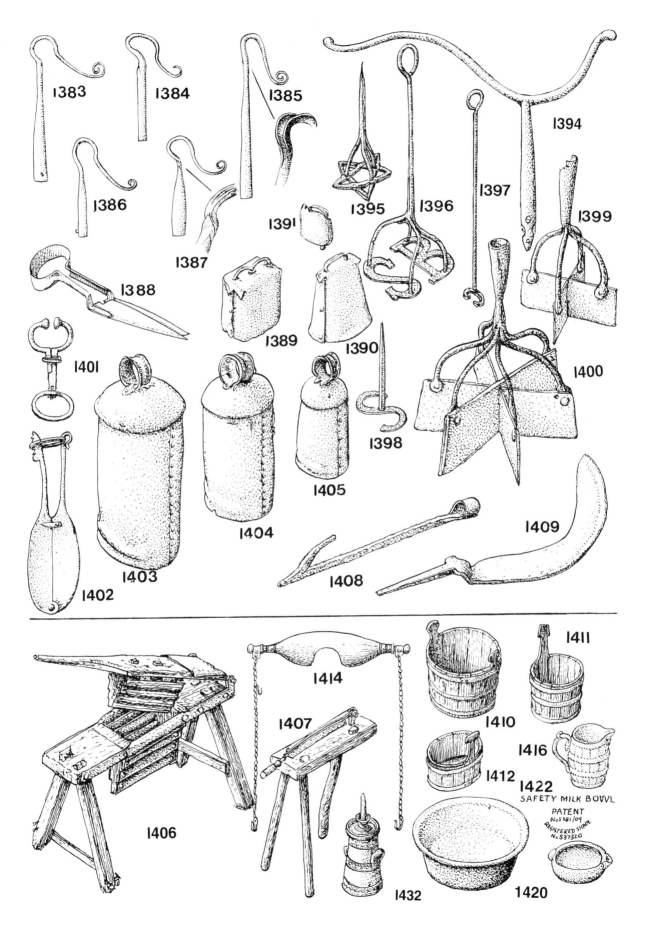

1383

1384

1385

1386

1387

1391

1395

1396

1397

1394

1399

1388

1389

1390

1401

1398

1400

1404

1405

1402

1403

1409

1408

1414

1411

1407

1410

1406

1412

1416

1422

1432

SAFETY MILK BOWL
PATENT
No 5381/09
REGISTERED SHAPE
No 537320

1420

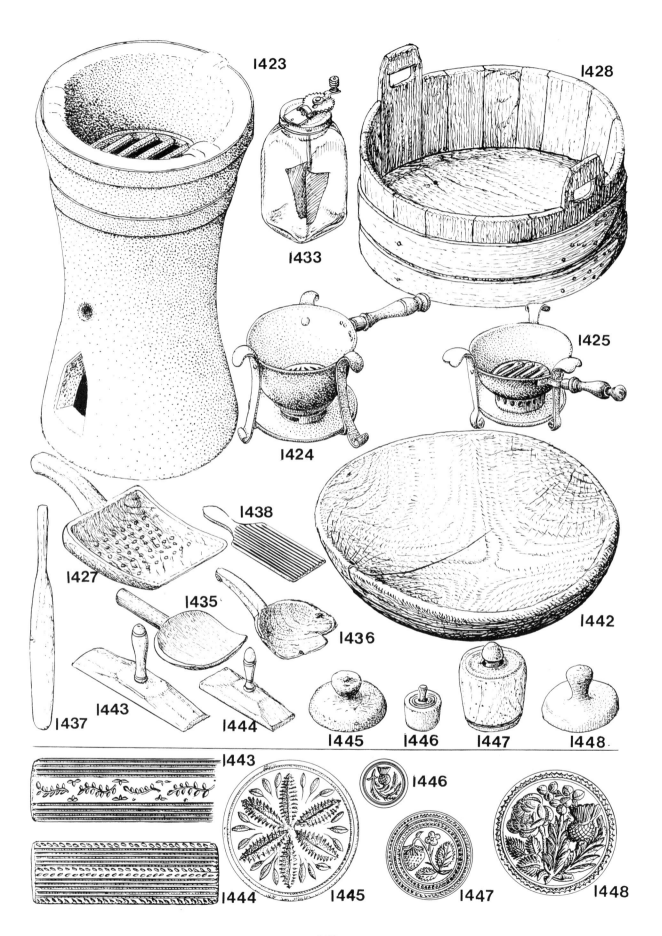

1423

1428

1433

1425

1424

1438

1427

1435

1436

1442

1437

1443

1444

1445

1446

1447

1448

1443

1446

1444

1445

1447

1448

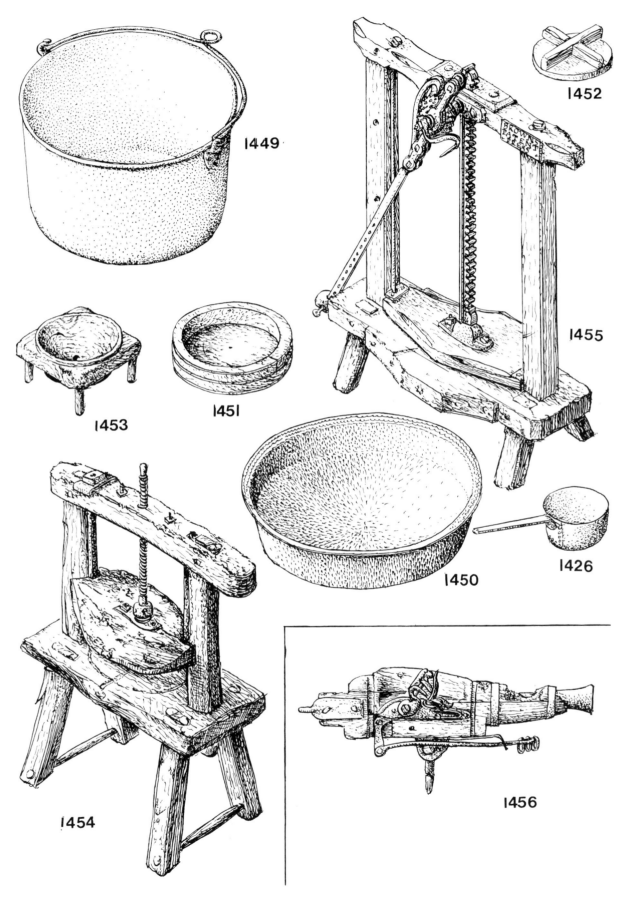

1449

1452

1455

1453

1451

1450

1426

1454

1456

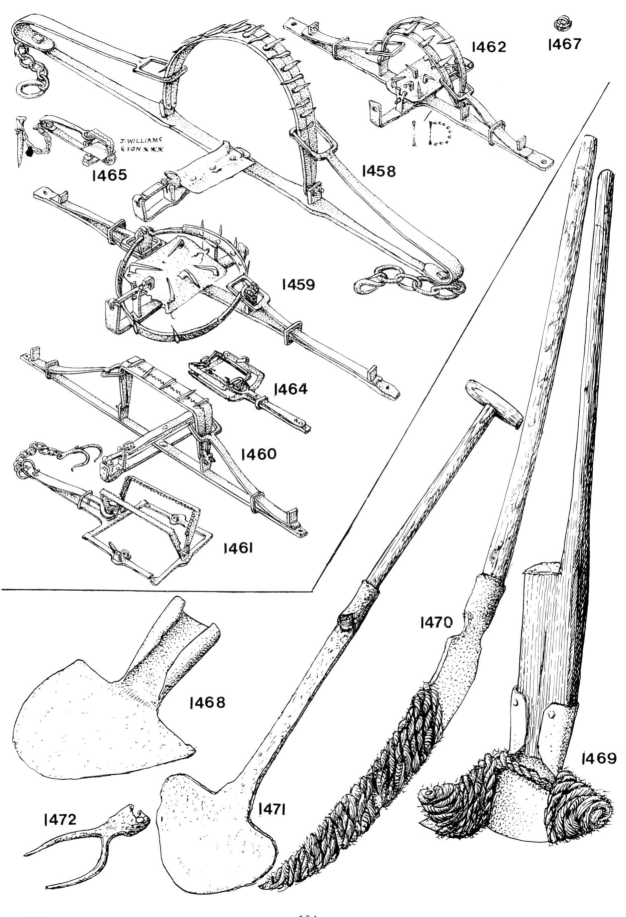

1462

1467

1465

J.WILLIAMS
& SON ✱✱✱

1458

1459

1464

1460

1461

1468

1472

1471

1470

1469

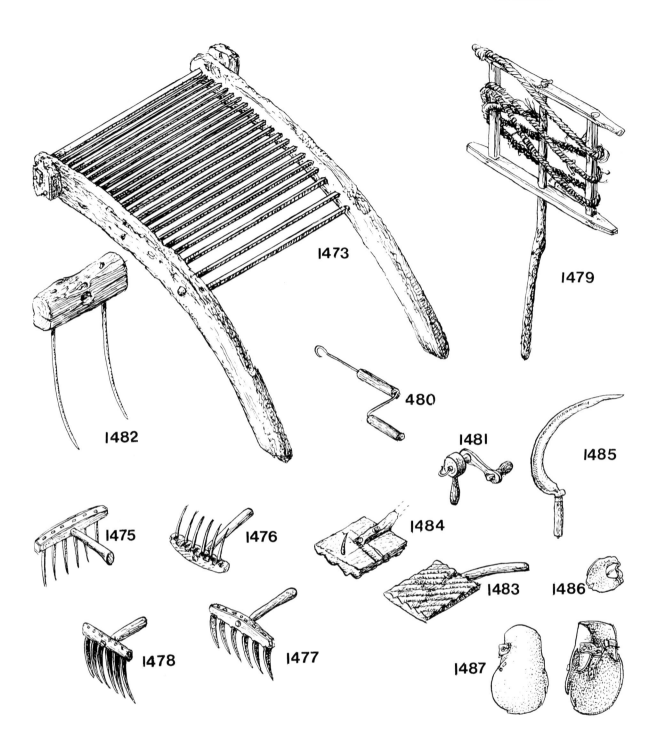

1473

1479

1482

480

1481

1485

1475

1476

1484

1483

1486

1478

1477

1487

Index to Manufacturers

numbers refer to the catalogue entries

Provenance Index

numbers refer to the catalogue entries